MARY ELIZABETH BRADDON

THE OCTOROON;
OR,
THE LILY OF LOUISIANA

Edited with an introduction by
JENNIFER CARNELL

HASTINGS
THE SENSATION PRESS
1999

This edition published in the United Kingdom in 1999
The Sensation Press
116 Sedlescombe Road North
Hastings
East Sussex TN37 7EN
United Kingdom
Tel\Fax 01424 423780
e-mail: Sensationbooks@hotmail.com

The Octoroon; or, The Lily of Louisiana is an unabridged reprint from *The Halfpenny Journal*, vol. 1, 11 November 1861 – 17 March 1862.

A CIP catalogue record for this book is available from the British Library

ISBN 1 9025 8004 4

Printed in Great Britain

CONTENTS

INTRODUCTION

In recent years the reputation of Mary Elizabeth Braddon has been restored to some of the prominence she enjoyed for six decades. In the 1860s she was one of the most successful and controversial novelists of her generation, rated alongside Wilkie Collins as the inventor of the sensation genre. Admired and criticized in equal measure after the success of *Lady Audley's Secret* (1862), novel after novel flowed from her pen, often at the rate of two or three per year. Modern criticism has tended to concentrate on her most famous novel, *Lady Audley's Secret* (1862), and the subversive behaviour of its heroine. But her work is far more varied and complex than this early novel, both in her more mature works and the anonymous fiction she churned out for lower class magazines in the 1860s. The elements which were found to be controversial in her most famous novel are even more exaggerated in her anonymous fiction. Several of her mainstream novels have recently come back into print, but the serials she wrote for the most inexpensive magazines on sale in the early 1860s remain relatively uncharted. In December 1862 Braddon wrote to Edward Bulwer Lytton, her mentor and literary confidante:

> P.S. I do an immense deal of work which nobody ever hears of, for Halfpenny & penny journals. This work is most piratical stuff, & would make your hair stand on end, if you were to see it. The amount of crime, treachery, murder, slow poisoning, & general infamy required by the Halfpenny reader is something terrible. I am just going to do a little paracide (sic) for this week's supply.[1]

In that month the now famous and successful author of *Lady Audley's Secret* would have been completing the final monthly instalment of *Aurora Floyd* for *Temple Bar*, and the week's supply of 'paracide' must have been *The White Phantom*, which was appearing anonymously in the *Halfpenny Journal; A Magazine For All Who Can Read*.

At this time it was not widely known that Braddon was moonlighting amidst the mysterious world of lower class magazines and penny part novels, publications sold in small shops and tobacconists rather than respectable circulating libraries. However, the connection between sensation fiction and its humbler relations had already been made.

Early sensation fiction was seen to be influenced by working class fiction, and the characteristics of penny part fiction, known as penny bloods, were said to be infiltrating respectable serials and three volume novels. W. Fraser Rae, in his 1865 article 'Sensation Novelists - Miss Braddon' in the *North British Review*, commented that:

Others before her have written stories of blood and lust, of atrocious crimes and hardened criminals, and these have excited the interest of a very wide circle of readers. But the class that welcomed them was the lowest in the social scale, as well as in mental capacity. To Miss Braddon belongs the credit of having penned similar stories in easy and correct English, and published them in three volumes in place of issuing them in penny numbers. She may boast, without fear of contradiction, of having temporarily succeeded in making the literature of the Kitchen the favourite reading of the Drawing Room.[2]

Many critics differed with Rae over the simplistic language, and thought that Braddon was a talented writer wasting her time on rubbish. Braddon was unapologetic, and in *The Doctor's Wife* (1864) she created an author whose career echoed her own, and Sigismund Smith declares:

'What the penny public want, is plot, and plenty of it; surprises, and plenty of 'em; mystery, as thick as a November fog.'[3]

The irony, as Braddon must have known, was that this had also proved to be the case at the middle class circulating libraries. Bored with novels which acted almost as conduct books for young ladies, they welcomed sensation fiction and now enjoyed a plot with mystery and strong emotions. That the middle class shared this delight was a constant source of annoyance to critics, and authors of sensation fiction were blamed for supplying unsuitable fiction to satisfy the demand for novels of passion and crime. Braddon again made the point that there were similarities between the two readerships when Smith reappears in *The Ladies Mile* (1866) as Sigismund Smythe, and, like Braddon, he is now a writer of three volume novels. Despite the hostility of many critics, Braddon sold in great numbers, first in three volume form to the circulating libraries, and then in cloth or cheap yellowback reprints to the public. Her popularity with all classes was assured, and Rae complained: 'By the unthinking crowd she is regarded as a woman of genius.'[4]

The belief that fiction was becoming contaminated with crime, murders, and bigamy was a common one. The noble art of literature, which was meant to illuminate, was now being cheapened into becoming a form driven only by an urge to entertain, and worse still the influence was from working class entertainment. These working class readers were seen as mysterious and incomprehensible by the middle class journals, and were dubbed 'The Unknown Public' by Wilkie Collins.[5]

The serials they enjoyed were characterized with numerous incidents, in the way that sensation fiction was accused of doing, though naturally the penny part novels were much cruder and they genuinely do have an almost complete reliance on action over characterization. They consisted of about five pages per week, with the text set in double or triple columns, and a suitably dramatic illustration appeared at the top of each issue. There were numerous short paragraphs, little in the way of description or characterization, and dialogue took up most of the page. Braddon's work in this area was no exception; note, for example, her space filling in *The Octoroon*, she rarely missed the opportunity to use the full name of 'Don Juan Moraquitos'.

The fact that Braddon also wrote anonymous fiction, aimed at the poorest readers, has often been remarked on, but few have read any of these novels, partly because they are virtually unobtainable. The longest and most well known of these lower class serials by Braddon was *The Black Band; Or, The Mysteries of Midnight* (1861-1862), written under the pseudonym Lady Caroline Lascelles and running for fifty two weeks at two or three chapters per instalment. This enormous novel (240,000 words) of crime, secret societies, high society and low life is more typical of her anonymous output than *The Octoroon*, and the latter owes just as much to anti-slavery novels and stage melodramas of the period. In *The Doctor's Wife* (1864), Sigismund Smith describes his own novel in penny numbers, *The Smuggler's Bride*, proudly stating it 'teems with suicides':

There's the Duke of Port St. Martin's, who walls himself up in his own cellar; and there's Leonie de Pasdebasque, the ballet dancer, who throws herself out of Count Caesar Maraschetti's private balloon; and there's Lilia, the dumb girl, – the penny public like dumb girls, – who sets fire to herself from the – in fact, there's lots of them. (p.12)

Although one senses Braddon enjoyed the freedom to exercise her bent for melodramatic language and extraordinary incidents, it must also have been hard work, as she was often working on several serials at once. When Braddon began *The Octoroon* in November 1861, fame was still some time off, and this would arrive less than a year later with the publication of *Lady Audley's Secret* in three volumes by the Tinsley Brothers in September 1862. Her emergence as the 'queen of the circulating libraries' coincided with the success of the new publishers who took the risk and published her and other sensation novelists in the 1860s. Sensation fiction became associated with a new aggressive style of publishing, which eagerly sought publicity and courted notoriety.

Prominent among these new publishers was the man Braddon was to marry in 1874, John Maxwell (1824-1895), and the early part of her career as a novelist is inseparable from his.

John Maxwell was an orphan from Limerick, forced to make his own way in life when the trust fund which had supported him and his sisters was exhausted. He came to London when he was twenty years old at the request of the Irish poet Gerald Griffin to oversee an eight volume edition of his works, after which he worked briefly in journalism and insurance. At twenty five he was again dabbling in publishing, and the year before, in 1848, he married Mary Anne Crowley. Some time after the birth of their last child, Maxwell and his wife separated, due, apparently, to the mental instability of his wife. He founded a short lived newspaper, *Town Talk*, as early as 1858, and at some point he started to work in conjunction with the publishers Ward, Lock & Tyler.

Braddon and Maxwell met for the first time in April 1860, about five weeks after she had retired from the stage, and they renewed their acquaintance when she moved to London with her mother in the autumn of 1860. She soon became a contributor to the *Welcome Guest*, and to a new magazine he founded in July 1861.

The *Halfpenny Journal* was one of at least five lower class magazines Maxwell helped to found in the early eighteen sixties. It is now extremely scarce, probably because the paper quality was poor and many of its readers could not afford to have the weekly issues bound. With Braddon as chief contributor to the *Halfpenny Journal*, Maxwell was saved the expense of commissioning other writers, and Fanny Braddon, Mary Braddon's mother, assisted in an editorial capacity. Fanny Braddon was no ordinary Victorian mother: she had left her husband in about 1840 because of his financial and marital irregularities, and she supported her daughter throughout her theatrical career, travelling with her as 'Mrs. Seyton'. Fanny Braddon edited Maxwell's halfpenny magazine, replying to readers' problems and choosing poetry to print from unsolicited manuscripts. The correspondents wanted advice on their health, manners, the quality of their handwriting, and even sent locks of their hair to the editor for the colour to be officially determined in its columns.

The magazine was a co-production between Maxwell and Ward, Lock and Tyler, and was intended to compete with the brand leader and pioneer in this area, *Reynold's Miscellany*. It closely copied that magazine's format at half the price (and half the number of pages). The *Halfpenny Journal's* advice page included a new innovation on Reynolds's advice page: a matrimonial section in which readers sent in details and asked the editor to find them a spouse. Although condemned by some readers as horribly vulgar, this was clearly popular and today gives a wonderful insight into the aspirations and working habits of the 'unknown public,' who seem also to have included school boys, reasonably well educated young women, as well as those claiming an income of one hundred pounds per year. The *Halfpenny Journal* also followed Reynolds's paternalistic attitude towards its readers, and morality is extolled in the fiction and non fiction. Hard work, honesty, and good behaviour would be rewarded, and its readers were assured it was far better to be poor and virtuous than rich and corrupt. Despite this, in many ways, the plots would not have been considered moral enough by the standards of middle class fiction.

Even when Braddon became famous she continued to write anonymous novels for the penny public for several years, and abridged editions were published in America under her own name. When journals such as the *Athenaeum* discovered Braddon was the author of *The Black Band*, she received a great deal of criticism, not helped by Maxwell's attempts to deny she was the author. Critics might like to think that such fiction was only enjoyed by the working class, but the appearance of similar features in middle class fiction proved otherwise. Nor was the influence all one way, as the 'unknown public' also enjoyed Braddon's acknowledged works. *Lady Audley's Secret* was serialized a year after publication as a three decker in the lower class magazine the *London Journal*, and in 1866 it reprinted *Aurora Floyd*. The only obstacle for the lower classes was cost, they could not afford to join Mudie's circulating library, and had to wait until cheap reprints appeared.

After a few years Maxwell abandoned his attempt to provide popular literature in an affordable form to the poorer classes, and Braddon's fame and financial success in three volume form ensured she had no need to continue. Nevertheless, the influence of penny part fiction and the theatre left its mark on her middle class sensation fiction.

The Octoroon; or, The Lily of Louisiana was the second serial Braddon wrote for the *Halfpenny Journal*, and its arrival was announced in typically grand terms as 'An entirely original, powerful, and most truthful Romance':

The New Tale will be richly illustrated from actual scenes, sketched on the spot where the incidents depicted have happened. That "truth is stranger than fiction", every one has heard; and most people know that the success of "Uncle Tom's Cabin" is attributable to its marked adherence to fact and the hourly experience of every day life in Southern America. THE OCTOROON appeals straight to the heart and sympathies of every reader, however circumstanced, or wherever placed in our social system. Therefore, let all our Subscribers unite in helping us to make this Tale known: for, upon their co-operation may turn the mitigation of Slavery, if not the total abolition of the hideous traffic in Human Beings that the exigencies of Slavery both foster and sustain.[6]

Readers were urged to 'Tell friends to order No. 21.' The call to recruit more readers was a frequent plea, and suggests that, despite his claims, Maxwell was already having problems with sales. A year later he was to be bankrupt.

The subject matter of *The Octoroon* was seemingly very different to anything hitherto published in the magazine, having an avowed social purpose. Since America was already at war, the novel is set the year before, and popular sentiment in Britain was firmly with the North. The choice of subject and title was the equivalent of a modern spoiler, timed to coincide with the success of another author, and a new play about to open in London. A footnote to the title on the first instalment explained the meaning of the title, and a disclaimer denied it was indebted to the playwright Dion Boucicault:

Octoroon signifies *eighth blood*, or the child of a Quadroon by a white. The word is asserted to be the invention of Mr. Boucicault, the dramatist, whose drama, "The Octoroon, or Life in Louisiana", is said to have introduced it into the American vocabulary. It is now generally adopted, and it is used in the United States and elsewhere to signify all the shades of colour lighter than the Quadroon. The tale appearing in this publication is not taken from the drama in question.[7]

Dion Boucicault's play had been performed at the Winter Garden Theatre in New York in early December 1859, but it was not performed in London until November 1861. A number of sources have been suggested for Boucicault's play, including Shirley Brook's *The Creole; or, Love's Fetters* which was performed at the Lyceum in London in 1847, and Captain Mayne Reid's three volume novel *The Quadroon; or, A Lover's Adventures in Louisiana* (1856). The theme was, in part, a revival of the fevered reception accorded to the publication of *Uncle Tom's Cabin; or, Life Among the Lowly* (1852). Harriet Beecher Stowe's novel appeared in eighteen different editions within a year of its publication in Britain, and it was even translated into Welsh. Among its many admirers was Queen Victoria, and the author was welcomed with adulation when she visited Britain in 1853. Another novel popular with British readers was Richard Hildreth's *The White Slave; or, Memoirs of a Fugitive*, set in Virginia with a male Octoroon slave as its hero. Hildreth originally published his novel in 1836 as *The Slave; or, Memoirs of*

Archy Moore, but after Stowe's success he expanded it under a new title and a British edition of 1852 was dramatically illustrated by Charles Keene, including one plate of a slave auction. Braddon may well have read all these, but if she read the work of the black writer Frederick Douglas, whose *Narrative* went through a number of editions and who lectured in England and Scotland some years earlier, it did not influence her own tale of slavery.

On the whole her depiction of race imitates that of other writers. Those who are light enough to pass as white, like Eliza and George in *Uncle Tom's Cabin*, are the most rebellious, and the whiteness of Cora's skin is frequently emphasized. Wholly black characters are either like Toby and Sambo, passive and child-like, devoted to their masters, or, like Tristan, more influenced by his African nature, with something wild and untamed about him.

Naturally Braddon's novel has limitations, set in a country she had never seen, but then, as later, she was always willing to turn her hand to anything. Factual information could be derived from Harriet Beecher Stowe's *The Key to Uncle Tom's Cabin* (1853), and probably her recollection of plays she had seen or acted in provided some of the inspiration. Both the attempt at Negro and American dialogue seem similar to plays of the period. Nor, unlike Harriet Beecher Stowe, does she particularly promote a religious agenda, other than the token sentiments which were part and parcel of anti-slavery literature. Instead she advises the reader and her characters to trust in Providence, a theatrical as much as a religious tradition.

Braddon's novel is certainly more akin to melodrama than anti-slavery literature. The title was used to exploit the title and popularity of Boucicault's play, but Braddon also had some direct experience of the issues as presented by earlier plays. As an actress she almost certainly appeared in a stage version of *Uncle Tom's Cabin* in the early 1850s, and later she acted with the famous African American actor Ira Aldridge in *The Slave* (1818) by Thomas Morton, (also known under its earlier title *The Ethiopian; or, the Quadroon of the Mango Grove)* in which Aldridge played Gambia, the loyal slave. The play was set in Surinam in the West Indies, and Braddon played the Quadroon heroine, Zelinda, who, like Cora in *The Octoroon*, is the object of a villain's lust.

Although it has been stated by her biographer and others that Braddon's serial was directly based upon Boucicault's play, this is not the case. In fact, as shall be seen, its origins are more complex, with links to another melodrama performed at the same time. Naturally there are intentional similarities with Boucicault's play, but Braddon's is a different story. Both Boucicault's Zoe and Braddon's Cora are put up for sale through skullduggery, but, unlike Zoe, at first Cora has no idea she is an Octoroon, the identity of her mother having been kept a secret from her. Although the plots are not the same, similarities were suggested to the purchaser of the *Halfpenny Journal*, particularly through the illustrations, one promising a riverboat scene (the spectacular steamboat wreck in Boucicault's play was one of the most sensational scenes seen on the stage), and another of the heroine being sold at a slave auction, and instead of the wicked overseer M'Closky, Braddon provided a wicked usurer. It would seem, therefore, that Braddon's *Halfpenny Journal* serial was designed to coincide with the opening of Boucicault's play; in fact it preceded it, the serial began on 11 November, the play opened at the Adelphi on the 18 November.

Boucicault's play opened 'After repeated delays,'[8] allowing plenty of time for rivals to pre-empt him. Shortly before, at the Pavilion Theatre, Whitechapel, a play opened entitled *Louisiana; or, The Slave Daughter*, also known as *Cora; or, The Octoroon Slave of Louisiana*. The theatrical newspaper *The Era* described it as a 'startling drama.'[9] The similarities to Braddon's novel are compelling, with a 'slave daughter' called Cora and a slave called Toby. Yet this play contains central characters not in the serial: 'Curtis, an Abolitionist', 'Mike Murphy, a warm-hearted Irishman', George Danham, Lucy Johnson and Mrs. Corbet. It also depicted a spectacular fire on board a steamer, from which slaves were rescued, and clearly this was meant to rival the forthcoming scene in Boucicault's play. *Cora; or, The Octoroon Slave of Louisiana* was written by the theatre manager's son, John Douglas Jr. The performance was followed by a troupe of performing dogs, and the last play of the evening was *The Black Band; or, The Mysteries of Midnight*. This version of *The Black Band* was definitely based on Braddon's serial, as it was recommended to the readers of the *Halfpenny Journal*:

"The Black Band" has been dramatized, and is now performing, with great success, at the Royal Pavilion Theatre, Whitechapel.[10]

The exact relationship between the Pavilion theatre and the magazine may never be known. Perhaps Braddon sold a rough idea of what she was going to do in her serial to the theatre, and then Douglas wrote his own version from it; or perhaps, in exchange for allowing the dramatization of *The Black Band*, Braddon decided to use John Douglas's play about Cora, the Octoroon, as a basis for her serial. Either way, there must have been some sort of agreement, and certainly when the Pavilion mounted its production of *The Black Band*, the serial was far from complete, having a further seven months of installments to come, suggesting the theatre used what she had written so far, and either added to the plot or knew what was going to happen. Both serial and Pavilion drama were intended to take some of Boucicault's sales, and it is an irony that Braddon, who was to become incensed when playwrights and managers used her ideas without permission, happily did so herself.

The plot of the *Halfpenny Journal* serial remains dominated by more typical Braddon conflicts: concealed identities, plots, forbidden love, stolen wealth. Braddon's interest in slavery is cursory. Naturally Britain is held up as an example of freedom and democracy, conveniently ignoring its earlier involvement in the slave trade. This patriotism was also a feature of John Douglas's play, *The Era* commenting 'the merits of our own land (were) painted in too brilliant colours.'[11] Pauline Corsi, like Lady Audley, is a pretty blonde governess with a past, and could have belonged to any of her other works of the period. Camillia falls victim, as does the unbelievably gullible Clara (twice) in *The Black Band*, to a prospective seducer's kidnapping plot and, in true melodrama fashion, threatens to injure herself rather than her abductor. Although the dialogue and pacing resemble melodrama, this was a cause for criticism even in her three volume novels:

> The world is essentially a *stage* to Miss Braddon, and all the men and women, the wives, the lovers, the villains, the sea captains, the victims, the tragically jealous, the haters, the avengers, merely players. We could extract pages, fit as they stand, for the different actors in a melodrama, vehemently and outrageously unnatural.[12]

Unlike the original stage version of *The Octoroon*, Braddon does not deny her heroine a happy ending. Boucicault's Zoe, much to the dismay of London audiences and critics, committed suicide. Boucicault defended his decision, arguing the subject was too serious to warrant the conventional conclusion:

> In the death of the Octoroon lies the moral and the teaching of the whole work. Had this girl been saved, and the Drama brought to a happy end, the horrors of her position, irremediable from the very nature of the institution of slavery, would subside into the condition of temporary annoyance.[13]

Soon Boucicault relented under the pressure from press and public, and a new ending, in which Zoe escaped, was added by 14 December 1861. Eventually Braddon has two Octoroons when one of the other characters learns he is of mixed blood. Braddon promotes miscegenation, but only between characters who look white. A romance between Tristan and Camillia would have been too radical, and Cora continues to treat Toby as an inferior, even when she learns her status is the same as his.

The Octoroon is the shortest of Braddon's serials in the *Halfpenny Journal*, written concurrently with *The Black Band*, and even if it cannot be regarded as a serious contribution to abolitionist literature, it remains an interesting example of the influence of contemporary drama on popular fiction.

NOTES

1. Letter from Braddon to Bulwer Lytton, December 1862: reproduced in Robert Lee Wolff, 'Devoted Disciple: The Letters of Mary Elizabeth Braddon to Sir Edward Bulwer Lytton 1862-1873', *Harvard Library Bulletin*, vol. 12 (1974), 5-35 and 129-161, p.11. Quoted by permission of Hertfordshire Archives and Local Studies, (D/ELC12/119).

2. W.F. Rae, 'Miss Braddon', *North British Review*, vol. 43, September 1865, p.204.

3. M.E. Braddon, *The Doctor's Wife* (London: Maxwell, 1864; repr. Oxford: Oxford University Press, 1998), p.45.

4. Rae, p.180.

5. Wilkie Collins, 'The Unknown Public', *Household Words*, 21 August 1858, pp.217-222.

6. *Halfpenny Journal*, vol. 1, 11 November 1861, p.160.

7. *Halfpenny Journal*, vol. 1, 18 November 1861, p.161.

8. *The Era*, 24 November 1861, p.10.

9. *The Era*, 17 November 1861, p.11.

10. 'To Correspondents', *Halfpenny Journal*, vol. 1, 6 January 1862, p.224.

11. *The Era*, 17 November 1861, p.11.

12. 'Our Female Sensation Novelists', *Christian Remembrancer*, vol. 46, 1863, p.236.

13. Letter from Dion Boucicault to *The Times*, quoted in *The Era*, 24 November 1861, p.5.

SELECT BIBLIOGRAPHY

Boucicault, Dion, *Plays by Dion Boucicault* (Cambridge: Cambridge University Press, 1984)

Disher, Maurice Willson, *Blood and Thunder: Mid-Victorian Melodrama and its Origins*, (London: Frederick Muller, 1949)

Hughs, Winifred, *The Maniac in the Cellar: Sensation Novels of the 1860s*, (Princeton: Princeton University Press, 1980)

James, Louis, *Fiction for the Working Man 1830-1850*, (Oxford: Oxford University Press, 1963)

Pykett, Lyn, *The Women's Sensation Novel and the New Woman Writing*, (London: Routledge, 1992)

Wolff, Robert Lee, *Sensational Victorian: The Life and Fiction of Mary Elizabeth Braddon*, (New York and London: Garland, 1979)

Wolff, Robert Lee, '*Devoted Disciple: The Letters of Mary Elizabeth Braddon to Sir Edward Bulwer Lytton, 1862-1873*', *Harvard Library Bulletin*, vol. 12 (1974), pp.5-35 and pp.129-161

NOTE ON THE TEXT

The Octoroon; or, The Lily of Louisiana was serialized anonymously in
the first volume of the *Halfpenny Journal* in weekly instalments from
Monday 11 November 1861 to Monday 17 March 1862. On such a
magazine it would not have been financially worthwhile to commission
original illustrations, and they were probably taken from an American
source. The illustrator was called Etherington. Edmund Yates once
related that for one of the first jobs he did for Maxwell, he had to fit a
fictional account of the crimes of the poisoner William Palmer to a set of
improbable pictures. Certainly some of the incidents in the novel, Paul
Lisimon reading the Gospel, for example, seem to be included to fit the
picture.

This edition has been taken unabridged from the *Halfpenny Journal*,
and retains all of the original illustrations. An American edition was
published by DeWitt in 1869. The text of the DeWitt edition is
presumably the same as other American editions, and the *Halfpenny
Journal* serialization has been compared to an 1895 American edition
published by Henry Altemus of Philadelphia. This reveals a slight
abridgment: the chapter 'The Lawyer's Map of the United States' is
missing and the previous chapter has been divided to form two, creating
a chapter called 'A Family Party'. There are a few other minor
differences but, on the whole, the American edition has only been used to
correct a few errors, as, for example, when Braddon was mistaken as to
which state New Orleans is in (in the serial she sometimes wrote it was in
Virginia).

CONTENTS

CHAPTER I.
CORA.

THE BELLE OF THE SOUTH

The last notes of a favourite waltz resounded through the splendid saloons of Mrs. Montresor's mansion in Grosvenor Square; sparkling eyes and glittering jewels flashed in the lamplight; the rival queens of rank and beauty shone side by side upon the aristocratic crowd; the rich perfumes of exotic blossoms floated on the air; brave men and lovely women were met together to assist at the farewell ball given by the wealthy American, Mrs. Montresor, on her departure for New Orleans with her lovely niece, Adelaide Horton, whose charming face and sprightly manners had been the admiration of all London during the season of 1860.

The haughty English beauties were by no means pleased to see the sensation made by the charms of the vivacious young American, whose brilliant and joyous nature contrasted strongly with the proud and languid daughters of fashion who entrenched themselves behind a barrier of icy reserve, which often repelled their admirers.

Adelaide Horton was a gay and light-hearted being. Born upon the plantation of a wealthy father, the cries of beaten slaves had never disturbed her infant slumbers; for the costly mansion in which the baby heiress was reared was far from the huts of the helpless creatures who worked sometimes sixteen hours a day to swell the planter's wealth. No groans of agonised parents torn from their unconscious babes; no cries of outraged husbands, severed from their newly-wedded wives, had ever broken Adelaide's rest. She knew nothing of the slave trade; as at a very early age the planter's daughter had been sent to England for her education. Her father had died during her absence from America, and she was thus left to the guardianship of an only brother, the present possessor of Horton Ville, as the extensive plantation and magnificent country-seat were called.

On Adelaide attaining her eighteenth year, her aunt, Mrs. Montresor, an inhabitant of New York, and the widow of a rich merchant, had crossed the Atlantic at Augustus Horton's request, for the purpose of giving her niece a season in London, and afterwards escorting her back to Louisiana.

She found Adelaide all that her most anxious relatives could have wished – elegant, accomplished, fashionable, well-bred; a little frivolous, perhaps, but what of that, since her lot in life was to be a smooth and easy one. Mrs. Montresor was delighted, and expressed her gratification very warmly to the Misses Beaumont, of West Brompton, in whose expensive but fashionable seminary Adelaide had been educated.

In an ante-chamber leading out of the crowded ball-room – an ante-chamber where the atmosphere was cool, and where the close neighbourhood of a fountain plashing into its marble basin in an adjoining conservatory refreshed the wearied ear, two young men lounged lazily upon a satin-covered couch, watching the dancers through the open ball-room door.

The first of these young men was a South American, Mortimer Percy, the partner of Augustus Horton, and the first cousin of the planter and his pretty sister Adelaide.

Mortimer Percy was a handsome young man. His fair curling hair clustered round a broad and noble forehead; his large clear blue eyes sparkled with the light of intellect; his delicate aquiline nose and chiselled nostrils bespoke the refinement of one who was by nature a gentleman; but a satirical expression spoiled an otherwise beautiful mouth, and an air of languor and weariness pervaded his appearance. He seemed one of those who have grown indifferent to life, careless alike of its joys and sorrows.

His companion contrasted strongly with him both in appearance and manner. With a complexion bronzed by exposure to Southern suns, with flashing black eyes, a firm but flexible mouth, shaded with a silky raven moustache, and thick black hair brushed carelessly back from his superb forehead, Gilbert Margrave, artist, engineer, philanthropist, poet, seemed the very type of manly energy.

The atmosphere of a crowded ball-room appeared unnatural to him. That daring spirit was out of place amidst the narrow conventionalities of fashionable life; the soaring nature needed wide savannahs and lofty mountain tops, distant rivers and sounding waterfalls; the artist and poet mind sighed for the beautiful – not the beautiful as we see it in a hot-house flower, imprisoned in a china vase, but as it lurks in the gigantic cup of the *Victoria regia* on the broad bosom of the mighty Amazon.

But Gilbert Margrave was one of the lions of 1860. An invention in machinery, which had enriched both the inventor and the cotton spinners of Manchester, had made the young engineer celebrated, and when it was discovered that he belonged to a good Somersetshire family, that he was handsome and accomplished, an artist and a poet, invitations flocked in upon him from all the fashionable quarters of the West-end.

He had been silent for some time, his gaze riveted upon one of the brilliant groups in the ball-room, when Mortimer Percy tapped him lightly on the shoulder with his gloved hand.

"Why, man, what are you dreaming of?" he said, laughing; "What entrancing vision has enchained your artist glance? What fairy form has bewitched your poet soul? One would think you were amid the solitudes of some forest on the banks of the Danube, instead of a ball-room in Grosvenor Square. Confess, my Gilbert, confess to your old friend, and reveal the nymph whose spells have transformed you into a statue."

Gilbert smiled at his friend's sally. The two young men had met upon the Continent, and had travelled together through Germany and Switzerland.

"The nymph is no other than yonder lovely girl, talking to your cousin, Miss Horton," said Gilbert; "look at her, Mortimer, watch the graceful head, the silky raven hair, as she bends down to whisper to her companion. Is she not lovely?"

Few who looked upon the young girl, of whom Gilbert Margrave spoke, could well have answered otherwise than in the affirmative. She was indeed lovely! In the first blush of youth, with the innocence of an angel beaming in every smile; with the tenderness of a woman lying shadowed in the profound depths of her almond-shaped black eyes. Features, delicately moulded and exquisitely proportioned; a tiny rose-bud mouth; a Grecian nose; a complexion fairer than the ungathered lily hiding deep in an untrodden forest: it was difficult for the imagination of the poet, or the painter, to picture aught so beautiful.

"Is she not lovely?" repeated Gilbert Margrave.

The young South American put his head critically on one side, with the calculating glance with which a connoisseur in the fine arts regards a valuable picture. The used-up Mortimer Percy made it a rule never to commit himself by admiring any thing, or any body.

"Hum – ha!" he muttered thoughtfully; "yes, she's by no means bad-looking."

"By no means bad-looking!" cried Gilbert Margrave, impatiently; "you cold-hearted automaton, how dare you speak of womanly perfection in such a manner. She's an angel, a goddess – a syren – a –"

"You'll have an attack of apoplexy, Margrave, if you go on in this way," said Mortimer, laughing.

"Can you tell me who she is?"

"No. But I can do more. I can tell you *what* she is."

"What do you mean?"

"I mean that your angel, your nymph, your goddess, your syren is – a slave."

"A slave?" exclaimed Gilbert.

"Yes. The African blood runs in those purple veins. The hereditary curse of slavery hovers over that graceful and queen-like head."

"But her skin is fairer than the lily."

"What of that? Had you been a planter, Gilbert, you would have been able to discover, as I did, when just now I stood close to that lovely girl, the fatal signs of her birth. At the extreme corner of the eye, and at the root of the finger nails, the South American can always discover the trace of slavery, though but *one drop* of the blood of the despised race tainted the object upon whom he looked."

"But this girl seems an intimate friend of your cousin, Adelaide; who can she be?" asked Gilbert.

"Yes, that is the very thing that puzzles me. Adelaide must be utterly ignorant of her origin, or she would never treat as a friend one who, on the other side of the Atlantic, would be her lady's maid. But, hush, here comes my aunt, she will be able to tell us all about her beautiful guest."

Mrs. Montresor was still a handsome woman. She bore a family likeness to her nephew, Mortimer, who was the only son of her sister, while Adelaide and Augustus Horton were the children of her brother. Her fair ringlets had, as yet, escaped the hand of Time. No tell-tale streaks of grey had stolen amid the showering locks. Her blue eyes were as bright as those of a girl, and shone with the light of good humour and benevolence. She was not only a handsome woman, she was a loveable one. The young instinctively clung to her, and felt that within that ample bosom beat a kindly heart, which a long summer of prosperity had never rendered callous to the woes of others.

"Come, gentlemen!" she said gaily, as she approached the two friends; "this is really too bad! Here you are lolling on a sofa, 'wasting your sweetness on the desert air,' while I have, at least, half a dozen pretty girls waiting for eligible partners for the next waltz. As for you,

Mortimer," she added, shaking her perfumed fan, threateningly at her nephew; "you are really incorrigible; poor Adelaide does not even know you are here."

"I came in late, my dear aunt, and I saw that both you and my cousin were so surrounded by admirers, it was quite impossible to approach you."

"A pretty excuse, sir, which neither I nor Adelaide will accept," said Mrs. Montresor, laughing.

"And then, again, I wanted to have a chat with Gilbert."

"Out upon your gallantry, sir; you preferred talking to Mr. Margrave to dancing with your cousin and affianced bride?"

"I am not a very good dancer; I am apt to tread upon the ladies' lace flounces, and get my heels entangled in the spurs of young dragoons. I really thought my cousin would rather be excused."

"Indeed, sir," exclaimed Mrs. Montresor, evidently rather annoyed by her nephew's indifference; "I should not be surprised if Adelaide should one day ask to be excused from marrying you."

"Good gracious!" cried Mortimer, playing with his watch-chain; "do you think my cousin is not very violently in love with me?"

"Violently in love with you? coxcomb! But, joking apart, really, Mortimer, you are the coldest, most unpoetical, soulless creature I ever met with."

"My dear aunt," said Mortimer, apologetically, "I will freely own that I am not a very sentimental person. But what of that? My intended marriage with my cousin, Adelaide, is by no means a romantic affair. In the first place, Augustus Horton and I are partners. My marriage with his sister is therefore advisable, on the ground of commercial interests. That is reason, number one, not very romantic to begin with. Reason, number two, is this: you have two nephews and one niece; you wish your favourite nephew (meaning me), to marry your niece, in order, that one of these days, having no children of your own, you may leave them the bulk of your fortune. There's nothing particularly romantic in this. You say to the two young people, 'Marry!' and the two young people say, 'Very well, we're agreeable!' and behold, the business is settled. Very advisable, and very proper, no doubt, but not a subject for romance, my dear aunt."

"Bah, Mortimer, you're incorrigible; but I know that at the bottom of your heart you're very much in love with your pretty cousin, notwithstanding your pretended indifference."

"Come, then, my best of aunts. Forgive your most perverse of nephews, and answer me one question, for the benefit of Gilbert Margrave here, who has been bewitched by one of the lilies of your ball-room."

"Indeed, and pray who is the lady?"

"That is the very question we want you to answer," replied Mortimer, leading his aunt to the curtained doorway of the ball-room. "See, there she is, that dark-eyed girl, talking to my cousin Adelaide."

"That is Miss Leslie."

"What Miss Leslie?"

"The daughter of Mr. Gerald Leslie, of New Orleans."

"Indeed!" exclaimed Mortimer.

"Yes. But you seem surprised."

"I am a little," replied the young man, thoughtfully; "I did not know Leslie had a daughter."

"But you see he has, since she is an intimate friend of Adelaide's."

"How did they become acquainted?"

"They were educated at the same school."

"Indeed. She is a very lovely girl, and you must be good enough to introduce us to her, by-and-bye."

"Take care, Mortimer," said his aunt; "you are surely not going to fall in love with Miss Leslie."

"Not the least danger, my dear aunt. Though I would not say as much for poor Gilbert, here."

"Pshaw! Mortimer," exclaimed the young artist, reddening; "it is the painter's privilege to admire beauty without loving it."

"No doubt of it, my dear boy," answered Mortimer; "but, unfortunately, sometimes a certain little rosy-legged gentleman, with a bow and arrows, called Cupid, steps in; the *painter* forgets his privilege, and the *man* falls in love with the artist's model."

"Well, I must leave you, gentlemen," said Mrs. Montresor; "I think I see Adelaide and Miss Leslie coming this way, so if you want an introduction to the young South American you must obtain it through my niece. *Au revoir*, naughty boys!"

"Stay, my dear aunt, you will forgive Mr. Margrave when I tell you that he is as determined an abolitionist as yourself, or any of your friends in New York. He means sailing for South America in a month, armed with some new inventions in machinery, which he declares ought to supersede slave-labour."

"Yes, madam," said Gilbert, earnestly; "your nephew well knows my opinion upon this subject, and though his interests may be allied to the hateful barter, which should call a blush to the cheek of every honest American, I know that his heart is with us, the abolitionists of slavery."

"Let me shake hands with you, Mr. Margrave," exclaimed Mrs. Montresor; "I declare to you that so hateful to me is the slave trade, and all connected with it, that were it not necessary for me to escort my niece home and assist at her marriage with this hare-brained boy, I would never again set foot upon the accursed soil of Louisiana; but I must not say more to you now, for here come the young ladies. Adelaide is but a child as yet, and has never thought seriously of the matter; while her brother, Augustus, like his father before him, is a determined advocate of slavery. Once more, adieu!" and the elegant, although somewhat portly, Mrs. Montresor, glided from the room, her rich robes of sky-blue moiré antique rustling around her.

"Gilbert," said Mortimer, hurriedly, as soon as his aunt was out of hearing, "remember, I beg, do not breathe to a mortal one hint of what I just now told you, with regard to Miss Leslie's origin. I suspect some painful mystery here, and I would not, for the world, that any idle talk of mine should cause this poor girl's gentle heart one throb of sorrow, or one thrill of shame."

"You may rely upon me, Mortimer," exclaimed Gilbert, with enthusiasm. "My lips are sealed for ever."

He had scarcely spoken, when the two young girls approached, arm-in-arm.

There was a marked contrast between the two friends. Young as Adelaide Horton was, she had already all the finished elegance and easy confidence of a woman of fashion. Frivolous, capricious, and something of a coquette, she was born to charm in a ball-room, and to shine in a crowd. Cora Leslie was a creature of an utterly different nature. Like some wild flower from the luxuriant forests of her native South, she seemed destined to bloom with a sweeter perfume in loneliness. To blossom for the silent stars and the midnight skies; to expand her fairest petals to the sunshine of one loving heart.

"I do not care to see my cousin just now," said Mortimer, "so I will leave you, Gilbert, to make yourself agreeable to the young ladies, while I go and smoke a cigar in the balcony opening out of the conservatory."

The young man strolled through the curtained doorway, leading into the cool retreat, as his cousin and her friend entered from the ball-room.

"Here, at least, my dear Cora, we shall be able to breath," said Adelaide, as the two girls approached Gilbert. "Ah, Mr. Margrave," she added, perceiving the young artist, "it is here, then, that you have been hiding yourself while a hundred lion hunters have been trying to chase you. Cora, allow me to introduce to you Mr. Gilbert Margrave, engineer, artist, poet and – lion! Mr. Margrave, allow me to present to you Miss Cora Leslie, my friend, and the most elegant waltzer in my aunt's crowded assembly."

"I beg, Mr. Margrave," said Cora Leslie, "that you will not listen to Miss Horton's assertions; she only grants me this eulogy because she knows that she waltzes better than I."

"Will you permit me to be the judge of that, Miss Leslie," said Gilbert, "and, in order that I may be so, grant me your hand for the next waltz?"

"Oh, yes, yes," cried Adelaide, laughing, "we'll waltz with you. I promise for Cora. Now, pray go back into the ball-room, Mr. Margrave, and satisfy those good people who are pining to stare you out of countenance, which is the only English tribute to genius. Go now, you shall summon Cora as soon as the first notes of the waltz strike up."

"*Au revoir*, then, Miss Leslie, till I come to claim your hand."

Gilbert bowed and left the ante-room, not without one enthusiastic glance at the innocent face of the fair Louisianian.

"There goes another of your admirers, Cora," cried Adelaide, as she flung herself into one of the luxurious easy chairs, while Cora seated herself on a sofa, a few paces distant and laid her bouquet of hothouse-flowers on a tiny table at her side. "I declare, Miss Cora Leslie, that I begin to think I did a very unwise thing in persuading my dear, good-natured aunt to give this farewell *reunion* to our English friends, for you had only to make your appearance in order to steal every admirer I have. It is a general desertion to the camp of the enemy. I should not wonder if Mortimer himself joined the renegades, and left me to sing willow for my inconstant swain."

"But I thought from what you told me, Adelaide," replied Cora, laughing, "that Mr. Percy was by no means a very enthusiastic or romantic person."

"Oh, no indeed," said Adelaide, with an impatient sigh; "you are right there, my dear Cora, never was there such a cold-hearted, matter-of-fact being as that cousin and future husband of mine. If he pays me a compliment, it is only an artful way of drawing attention to one of my defects, which, I will own, are rather numerous. If he ever utters an affectionate word, I always feel convinced that he is laughing at me. Imagine now, my dear Cora, was it not flattering to my womanly vanity to hear him say, when he arrived in London a month or two ago, after a separation of four years, 'My dear Adelaide, my aunt has taken it into her head that you and I ought to marry; I don't want to oppose her, and I suppose you don't either.' "

"And you replied—?"

" 'Oh, no, my dear cousin; I've no objection to marry you. But pray don't ask anything else.' "

"But why did you give your consent?" asked Cora.

"I scarcely know. I am impetuous, rash, passionate, capable of doing even a wicked action when under the influence of some sudden impulse. I am daring enough, Heaven knows, but there is one species of courage that I lack – the courage which gives the power of resistance. I could not oppose my aunt. Has she not been the tenderest of mothers to me? Besides, I did not love anyone else, or at least—. Why abandon myself to dreams that can never be realized? Again, as the wife of my cousin Mortimer, I shall never be an exile from my dear native South. If you see me gay and happy, Cora, in spite of my approaching marriage, it is that I shall soon behold the blue skies of my beloved Louisiana."

"Forgive me, dearest Adelaide," said Cora Leslie, "but from a few words that escaped you just now, I fancy that I have a secret of your heart. Has Mr. Margrave, by any chance, made an impression in that quarter?"

"You are very inquisitive, Miss," replied Adelaide, blushing; "Mr. Margrave is an accomplished young man, but his manner to me has never gone beyond the bounds of the most ceremonious politeness. Perhaps, indeed, had he betrayed any warmer sentiment towards me, I might—. But do not, I implore you, force me to reflect, my dear Cora. Is it not decided that I am to marry Mortimer? I will present him to you this evening if he makes his appearance, and you shall tell me what you think of him."

"I am most impatient to see him," said Cora. "Tell me, dear Adelaide, did you ask him for tidings of my father?"

"Do not think me forgetful, dear Cora, but I had so much to say to him about my brother and my native country, that I forgot to make the enquiries you charged me with. There now, you are angry with me, I know, I can see it in your eyes."

"No, Adelaide, no!" answered Cora, "that which you see in my eyes is not anger, but anxiety. It is nearly three months since I have received any letter from my dear father, and this long silence is so unlike his affectionate consideration that it has filled me with alarm."

"Nay, my dear Cora, the cares of business no doubt have prevented his writing; or perhaps he is coming over to England, and wishes to give you a delightful surprise. Did you not tell me that Mr. Leslie meant to sell his plantation, and take up his abode in England? But here comes Mortimer, and you can yourself make all the enquiries you wish."

CHAPTER II.
THE FATAL RESOLVE.

The young planter strolled with a leisurely step through the doorway of the conservatory, bowing to the two girls as he entered the room.

"At last!" exclaimed Adelaide; "so you have actually condescended to honour my aunt's assembly with your gracious presence, my dear cousin. Perhaps you were in hopes you would not see me."

"Perhaps you were in hopes I should not come," retorted the young man.

"On the contrary," said Adelaide, "I was awaiting you with impatience. But pray don't be alarmed, it was not on my own account, but on that of Miss Leslie that I wished to see you. My friend is anxious to ask you about her father."

"I was just about to beg you to introduce me to Miss Leslie," replied Mortimer.

"Mr. Mortimer Percy, cotton merchant and slave proprietor, my cousin and my future husband, as my aunt says—"

"Stop, Adelaide, this is no time for jesting," said Mortimer, gravely.

"Is your news bad, then?" exclaimed his cousin.

"It is not altogether as favourable as I should wish."

"Oh, in Heaven's name, speak, Mr. Percy," cried Cora, pale with agitation, "what has happened to my father?"

"Reassure yourself, Miss Leslie," replied Mortimer, "when I left New Orleans your father was rapidly recovering."

"He had been ill, then?"

"He was wounded in a revolt of the slaves on his plantation."

"Wounded!" exclaimed Cora; "oh, for pity's sake, do not deceive me, Mr. Percy! this wound – was it dangerous?"

"It was no longer so when I left Louisiana, I give you my honour."

Cora sank into a chair, and buried her face in her hands.

"You see, Adelaide," she murmured, after a few moments' silence, "my presentiments were not unfounded. Dearest father, and I was not near to watch and comfort you!"

Adelaide Horton seated herself by the side of her friend, twining her arm affectionately about Cora's slender waist.

"Strange," thought Mortimer Percy, as he watched the two girls, "one word from me, and my cousin would shrink from this lovely and innocent creature with loathing and disdain."

The prelude of a waltz resounded at this moment from the orchestra, and Gilbert Margrave appeared to claim his partner.

"Ah!" exclaimed Adelaide, "it is you, Mr. Margrave? My poor friend has just heard some sad news."

"Sad news, Miss Horton!"

"Yes, there has been a revolt of the slaves, in which her father well nigh fell a victim. Thank Heaven, the result was less terrible than it might have been."

While Adelaide was speaking to Mr. Margrave, Mortimer Percy approached the chair on which Cora was seated, and bending over her for a moment said, in a low voice, "let me speak to you alone, Miss Leslie."

"Alone!" exclaimed Cora, with new alarm, then turning to Gilbert, she said, calmly, "I trust that you will be so kind as to excuse me, Mr. Margrave, and ask Adelaide to favour you with her hand for the next waltz, I wish to speak to Mr. Percy about this sad affair."

"Cora insists upon it, Mr. Margrave," said Adelaide, "and you must, therefore, resign yourself. But remember," she added, turning to Cora, "that we only consent on condition that we find you smiling and altogether restored to good spirits on your return. Now, Mr. Mortimer Percy, after this I suppose you will leave off praising the virtue of your pet negroes."

"What would you have, my dear cousin?" replied Mortimer; "when dogs are too violently beaten, they are apt to bite."

"They should be tied up then," retorted Adelaide as she took Gilbert's arm and hurried to the ball-room where the dancers were already whirling round in a *valse-à-deux temps*.

Cora rose as she found herself alone with the young planter, and no longer attempting to conceal her agitation, exclaimed anxiously,

"And am I indeed to believe what you say, Mr. Percy; do you really mean that it is ill-usage which has urged my father's slaves to this revolt?"

"Alas, Miss Leslie," replied the young South American, "the planter finds himself between the horns of a terrible dilemma; he must either beat his slaves or suffer from their laziness. I will own to you that Mr. Leslie is not considered too indulgent a master; but he only follows the example of the greater number of our colonists. However, it is not he, but his overseer who was the chief cause of this revolt. Your father would have interfered: in attempting to do so he was seriously wounded; but let me once more assure you that he was entirely out of danger when I left New Orleans."

"And did he give you no message for me – no letter?" asked Cora.

"No, Miss Leslie."

"What, not a word?"

"Your father did not know that I should see you," replied Mortimer, "and it is on this very subject that I wish to ask you a few questions; not prompted by any vain curiosity, believe me, but because you inspire me with the warmest interest."

"Speak, Mr. Percy," said Cora, seating herself.

Mortimer drew a chair to the side of that on which Cora was seated, and placing himself near to her, said gravely,

"Tell me, Miss Leslie, in what manner do you usually receive your father's letters?"

"Through one of his correspondents who lives at Southampton."

"Then they are not directly addressed to you."

"They are not."

"Were you very young when you left Louisiana?"

"I was only five years old," replied Cora.

"So young! Your memory can recall nothing that occurred at that time, I suppose."

"Oh, yes," answered Cora; "but memories so confused that they seem rather to resemble dreams. But there is one recollection which no time can efface. It is of a woman, young, beautiful, who clasped me to her arms, sobbing as she strained me to her breast. I can still hear her sobs when I recall that scene."

"Has Mr. Leslie ever spoken to you of your mother?" asked Mortimer.

"Was it she?" cried Cora, eagerly.

"I do not know, Miss Leslie, for at that time I was still in England, where, like you, I received my education."

"Alas," exclaimed Cora, her beautiful eyes filling with tears, "who could it be if it was not her? No, Mr. Percy, I have never known even the poor consolation of hearing people speak of my mother. Every time I have ventured to address my father on the subject, he has replied in harsh and cold tones that have chilled my heart. All that I could ever learn was that she died young, at New Orleans. I dared not speak upon a subject which caused my poor father such painful emotions."

"But he has always evinced the greatest affection for you, Miss Leslie, has he not?" asked Mortimer.

"Oh, Mr. Percy," replied Cora, her eyes kindling with enthusiasm, "what father ever better loved his child. Every whim, every childish wish has been gratified, but one; alas, that one prayer he would never grant."

"And that prayer was—?"

"That I might join him in New Orleans. On his first visit to England, a year ago, I implored him to take me back with him; but he was deaf to all my entreaties. 'It is because I love you,' he said, 'that I refuse to take you with me;' perhaps it was the climate of Louisiana that he feared; perhaps that climate may have been the cause of my mother's death."

"I was sure of it," thought Mortimer, "she is entirely ignorant of her origin."

"All that I could obtain from him in answer to my prayers," continued Cora, "was a promise that this separation should be the last; that he would sell his plantation at the earliest opportunity, and come and establish himself in England."

"And since then," said Mortimer, "has he renewed that promise?"

"With reservations that have made me tremble," replied Cora; "I feel that his affairs are embarrassed, and will detain him from me long after the promised time of our re-union."

"Alas, Miss Leslie, you are not deceived," said Mortimer, earnestly; "Mr. Leslie has experienced great losses. The death of Mr. Treverton, his partner, who was killed in a duel a year ago, at the very time of your father's return from England, revealed deficiencies that he had never dreamed of. He was obliged to have recourse to heavy loans; and since that, the revolt of his slaves, in damaging the harvest, has given the finishing blow to his difficulties."

"Then my father is ruined, Mr. Percy," cried Cora, clasping her hands: "oh, do not imagine that the aspect of poverty alarms me; it is not of myself that I think, but of him. What a life of anxiety and effort he has endured, in order to establish a position, which he only seemed to value on my account. Never has he allowed me to hear one expression of uneasiness drop from his lips; never has he denied the most extravagant of my caprices. Ah, if he but knew how gladly I would exchange all this worthless splendour for the happiness of sheltering my head upon his noble breast. If he could but tell how dear the humblest home would be to me after the long isolation of my youth. Who can tell now how long our separation may endure?"

"Nay, Miss Leslie," said Mortimer soothingly; "your father's position is far from desperate, though he may require a long time and considerable courage in order to extricate himself from his difficulties."

"A long time! Some years, perhaps?" asked Cora.

"I fear so."

"And during this heart-rending struggle," exclaimed the young girl, "he will not have a creature near him to comfort or to sustain him. And if new dangers should menace him − for this revolt has been avenged by the blood of the slave-leaders, has it not? − and fresh cruelties may cause new rebellion. Oh, Heaven! the thought makes me tremble! No, my father shall not be alone to struggle! If he suffers I will console him; if he is in danger I will share it with him."

"What do you mean, Miss Leslie?" cried Mortimer.

"You leave England in a few days with Mrs. Montresor and your cousin, Adelaide. I will accompany you."

"But, Miss Leslie, remember!" remonstrated the young man.

"I remember nothing but that my father is in danger, and that a daughter's place is by his side. See, here comes Mrs. Montresor, I know she will not refuse to grant my request."

The good-natured hostess had come to the ante-chamber to look after her wall-flowers, as she called them.

"You running away from us, Cora," she said; "we shall certainly not allow this matter-of-fact nephew of mine to deprive us of the belle of the room."

"Oh, my dear Mrs. Montresor," exclaimed Cora; "a great misfortune has happened to my father."

"I know it, my dear child," replied Mrs. Montresor; "but, thank Heaven, that misfortune is not an irreparable one."

"No, madam, nothing is irreparable, but the time which we pass far away from those we love in their hour of trouble. I implore you to take me back to him."

"But, Cora," answered Mrs. Montresor, "do you forget that your father formally expressed his wish that you should remain in England?"

"Yes, madam; but the motive of my disobedience will render it excusable, and my first duty is to go and console my father."

"Pardon me if I still interfere, Miss Leslie," said Mortimer Percy, earnestly; "but think once more before you take this rash step. Your father may have some very serious motive for forbidding your return to New Orleans."

"What motive could a father have for separating himself from his only child? But stay," added Cora, struck by the earnestness of Mr. Percy's manner, "perhaps there is some secret mystery which you are aware of. Tell me, sir, is it so? Your manner just now – the strange questions which you asked me, all might lead me to suppose—"

"Those questions were only prompted by my interest in you, Miss Leslie," replied Mortimer; "and it is the same interest which bids me urge you to abandon the thought of this voyage. Your father's welcome may not be as warm as you would wish."

"I know his heart too well to fear that," exclaimed the excited girl; "be it as it may, my resolution is irrevocable; and if you refuse to take me under your charge, Mrs. Montresor," she added, "I will go alone."

"What?" cried Adelaide, who had entered the ante-chamber, followed by Gilbert, in time to hear these last words. "You would go alone, Cora: and who, then, opposes your departure? We will go together; will we not, dear aunt?" exclaimed the impetuous girl.

"Yes, Adelaide, since your friend is determined on leaving, it will be far better for her to accompany us," replied Mrs. Montresor; "but I must own that I do not willingly give my consent to Miss Leslie's disobedience to her father's wishes."

"But my father's thanks shall repay you for all, dear madam," said Cora; "I shall never forget this goodness."

"Come, come, then, naughty child, let us return to the ball-room. You must bid adieu to all your acquaintance to-night, for our vessel, the Virginia, sails in three days. Come, children, come."

Mrs. Montresor led the two girls away, while Mortimer Percy flung himself on to a sofa, Gilbert Margrave watching him anxiously.

"Why did you not tell Mrs. Montresor the truth?" asked Gilbert.

"What would have been the use, since I cannot tell it to Miss Leslie? That is what seals my lips. Her father has concealed from her her real origin. She thinks she is of the European race – I discovered that in my interview with her – and I dare not reveal a secret which is not mine to tell."

"And you fear that her return to New Orleans will cause sorrow to herself," said Gilbert.

"I do," replied the young South American; "every door at which she dares to knock will be closed against her. Even my cousin, her friend, will turn from her with pity, perhaps, but with contempt. You, who dwell in a land where the lowest beggar, crawling in his loathsome rags, is as free as your mightiest nobleman, can never guess the terrors of Slavery. Genius, beauty, wealth, these cannot wash out the stain; the fatal taint of African blood still remains; and though a man were the greatest and noblest upon earth, the curse clings to him to the last. He is still – a slave!"

CHAPTER III.
THE USURER'S BARGAIN.

Cora's father, Gerald Leslie, was the owner of a fine estate upon the banks of a lake about two miles out of New Orleans, and also of a handsome house in that city. It is at this latter residence that we will introduce him to the reader.

Gerald Leslie was in the very prime of life. Scarcely yet forty-five years of age, time had set no mark upon his thick chestnut hair or his handsome face, save a few almost imperceptible wrinkles which the cares of the last year or two had drawn in rigid lines about his well-shaped mouth.

His features were massive and regular; the brow broad and intellectual; the large hazel eyes bright but yet thoughtful; and there was a shade of melancholy in the general expression of the countenance which lent a peculiar charm to the face of Gerald Leslie.

It was the face of one who had suffered. It was the face of one who had found himself a lonely man in the very prime of life; in that hour of all other hours in which a man yearns for the smiles of loving eyes, the warm pressure of friendly hands. It was the face of one who had discovered too late that he had sacrificed the happiness of his life to a mistaken principle.

While the good ship Virginia is sailing away from the dim blue shores of the fading English coast, bearing Mrs. Montresor, her nephew and niece, and Cora Leslie, to their far Southern home, let us enter the planter's luxuriously furnished study, and watch him as he bends over his desk.

The burning Southern sun is banished from the apartment by means of Venetian Shutters; the floor is covered with a cool matting woven from Indian reeds; and the faint plash of a fountain in a small garden at the back of the house is heard through one of the open windows.

It is not a pleasant task which occupies the planter. His brow contracts as he examines the papers, pausing every now and then to jot down two or three figures against a long row of accounts which look terribly formidable even to the uninitiated. At last he throws down a heap of documents with a weary sigh, and flinging himself back in his chair, abandons himself to gloomy thought.

"Yes, the truth is out at last," he muttered; "no hope of a settlement in England; no chance of a happy home on the other side of the blue Atlantic with my Cora, my only one. Nothing before me but the weary struggle of a ruined man, with difficulties so gigantic that, struggle as I may, they must close in upon me and crush me at the last. Oh, Phillip Treverton, but for the cruel deception you practiced upon me, I should not be in this position."

Philip Treverton was Gerald Leslie's late partner. He had been shot a twelvemonth before the opening of our story, in a sanguinary duel with a young Frenchman, who had insulted him in a gaming-house. But the two men had been more than partners, they had been friends; true and sincere friends; and Gerald Leslie no more doubted the honour of his friend, Phillip Treverton, than he would have doubted his own.

Amongst the debts owed by the two planters, there was one of no less than one hundred thousand dollars to a lawyer and usurer, one Silas Craig, a man who was both disliked and feared in New Orleans; for he was known to be a hard creditor, unscrupulous as to the means by which he enriched himself, pitiless to those who were backward in paying him.

In an evil hour Gerald Leslie and Philip Treverton had had recourse to this man, and borrowed from him, at a cruelly heavy rate of interest, the sum above mentioned. Treverton was, unlike his partner, a reckless speculator, and, unfortunately, not a little of a gamester; he therefore thought lightly enough of the circumstance. Not so Gerald Leslie. The thought of this loan oppressed him like a load of iron, and he was determined that it should be repaid at any sacrifice. He gathered together the money before leaving New Orleans to visit his daughter in England, and entrusted the sum to his partner, Treverton, with special directions that it should be paid immediately to Silas Craig.

Gerald Leslie knew that his partner was a gamester, but he firmly believed him to be one of the most honourable of men, and he had ever found him strictly just in all their commercial dealings.

He departed, therefore, happy in the thought that the debt was paid, and that Silas Craig, the usurer, could no longer rub his fat greasy hands, and chuckle at the thought of his power over the haughty planter, Gerald Leslie. He departed happy in the thought that his next voyage would be to convey him to an English home, where the tyranny of prejudice could never oppress his beloved and lovely child.

The first intelligence which greeted him on his return to New Orleans, was the death of his friend and partner.

Philip Treverton had died a week before Gerald Leslie landed. He had died at midnight in a wretched chamber at a gambling house. There was a mystery about his death – his last hours were shrouded in the darkness of the silent secrets of the night. None knew who had watched beside him in his dying moments. The murderer had escaped; the mutilated body of the murdered man was found in the waters of the Mississippi.

Philip Treverton's death was a sad blow to his survivor, Gerald Leslie. The two men had been associates for years; both thorough gentlemen, intellectual, highly educated, they had been united in the bonds of a sincere and heartfelt friendship.

What then were Gerald Leslie's feelings when he found that his friend, his partner, his associate, the man whom he had fully trusted, had deceived him; and that the money, left by him in Treverton's hands, had never been paid to Silas Craig?

In vain did he search amongst his friend's papers for the receipt; there was not one memorandum, not one scrap of paper containing any mention of the hundred thousand dollars; and a week after Gerald Leslie's return, he received a visit from the usurer, who came to claim his debt. The planter gave him a bill at a twelvemonth's date, the heavy interest for that period fearfully increasing the debt. This bill came due on the very day on which we have introduced Gerald Leslie to the reader, and he was now every moment expecting to hear the usurer announced. He was still without funds to meet his acceptance. Many other debts were pressing upon him; and he felt that in a few months his plantation must be sold and he, left a ruined man. But, as the drowning wretch catches at the feeblest straw, or the frailest plank, so he clung to the hope furnished by delay.

"Once more," he muttered, as he leaned his head upon his hands in the attitude of despair, "once more must I humiliate myself to this low-minded wretch, and beg the delay which he may grant or refuse, as it pleases his base nature. Heaven help me, I little dreamed that Gerald Leslie would ever come to sue to Silas Craig."

At this moment a cheerful-looking negro entered the apartment, bearing a card upon a silver salver.

"Massa Craig, please massa," he said.

"Tell him to walk in."

"Into this room, massa?"

"Yes, Caesar."

The negro departed, and in a few moments returned, ushering in a fat man, of about fifty years of age, dressed in the loose and light coloured coat and trousers, fashionable in New Orleans.

This summer costume, which was becoming to many, accorded ill with the fat and awkward figure of Silas Craig. The loose open collar displayed a bull neck that bespoke the brute force of a sensual nature. It was almost impossible to imagine a more truly repulsive appearance than that of the usurer of New Orleans; repulsive, not so much from natural ugliness, as from that hidden something, dimly revealed beneath the outward features that told the nature of the man, and caused the close observer and the physiognomist to shrink from him with instinctive abhorrence.

Cruelty leered out of the small rat-like grey eyes; hypocrisy and sensuality alike were visible in the thick lips and wide animal mouth. The usurer's hair, of a reddish yellow, was worn long, parted in the middle, and pushed behind his ears, giving a sanctimonious expression to his face. For it must be known to the reader that Silas Craig had always contrived to preserve a character for great sanctity. His voice was loudest in expressing horror at the backslidings of others; his presence was unfailing at the most frequented places of worship; and men who knew that the usurer would strip the widow or the orphan of the utmost farthing, or the last rag of clothing, beheld him drop his dollars into the plate at the close of every charity sermon.

By such pitiful artifices as these the world is duped, and Silas Craig was universally *respected* in New Orleans: respected in outward seeming by men who in their inmost soul loathed and execrated him.

With a bland smile, he obeyed Gerald Leslie's gesture, and seated himself in a low rocking-chair opposite the planter.

"Charming weather, Mr. Leslie," he said.

"Charming," answered Gerald, absently.

"I trust I see you well, my dear friend," murmured Silas Craig, in the fat, oily voice peculiar to him, "and yet," he added, almost affectionately, "I do not think you are looking well – no, decidedly not, you look a little harassed; a little care-worn, as if the business of this life was pressing too much upon you."

"I have good need to look harassed and care-worn," answered Gerald Leslie, impatiently. "Come, Mr. Craig, do not let us waste our time upon fine speeches, and sympathy which we cannot either of us be expected to feel – I know what you have come here for, and you know that I know it, so why beat about the bush? You have my acceptance, due to-day in your pocket, and you come to claim payment."

"You are as proud as ever, Mr. Leslie," said the usurer, an angry gleam shooting out of his small eyes, in spite of the affected smile upon his lips.

"Why should I be less proud than ever?" answered the planter, haughtily. "If you call a contempt for falsehood, and a loathing of hypocrisy pride, I am certainly amongst the proudest."

Gerald Leslie knew that every word he uttered was calculated to infuriate Silas Craig, and that, at the moment when he had to ask a favour of him; but the haughty spirit of the planter could less brook to stoop now than ever – the very fact of having to ask this favour stung him to the quick, and urged him on to show his contempt of the man from whom he had to ask it.

The usurer sat for some few moments in silence, rubbing his hands slowly, one over the other, and looking furtively at Gerald.

"You may ask me why you should be less proud today than ever, Mr. Leslie," he said, with a malicious grin. "Shall I tell you why? Because the tables are turned since the day when you passed Silas Craig in the streets of New Orleans, as if he had been one of the slaves on your plantation; when you spurned him as if he had been the dirt beneath your feet. I know what you said of me in those days; I came by my money by crooked ways; I was a rogue; an usurer; my ill-gotten wealth would bring me to the gallows some day. These are the sort of things you said, and I took them quietly enough; for I am of a patient disposition, and I knew my turn would come. It has come. The times are changed since then. My wealth was ill-gotten, was it? You were glad enough to borrow a hundred thousand dollars of it, ill-gotten as it was, and now when I come to-day to ask you for the payment of that money, you take such a high tone that I can only believe you have it ready for me in your cash-box yonder."

It was with a malicious chuckle that he uttered those concluding words; for the crafty wretch well knew the nature of Gerald Leslie, and he had suspected from the first that the money was not forthcoming.

"Not one penny of it!" cried the planter; "not one penny of it, Mr. Craig."

"Indeed!" said Silas. "Then I'm extremely sorry to hear it; as, of course, under those circumstances, I can no longer delay putting an execution upon your property, and sending the Leslie plantation and your valuable lot of niggers to the auctioneer's hammer."

Having uttered this threat, he sat for some little time with his hands on his knees, and a smile of triumph upon his face, watching the countenance of the planter.

Gerald Leslie's was a gloomy face to look upon in that moment; but it neither expressed grief nor humiliation, and his enemy was disappointed.

It was not enough to ruin the man he hated. Silas Craig would have given half his fortune to see that haughty spirit lowered in the dust.

The planter sat for some minutes in perfect silence, as if he were revolving some plan in his mind. Presently he looked up, and, without any alteration of his former manner, addressed the usurer thus:–

"Silas Craig, sooner than ask a favour of you, I would see every scrap of property I possess sold in the public sale-room, and would leave my native land a beggar. I do not ask you a favour, then; I offer you a bargain. If my property is sold to-day, it will be sold at a loss. *You* will be paid, it is true, but others, for whom (pardon me) I feel a great deal more concern, will lose. Two months hence that same property will, for certain commercial reasons known as well to you as to me, realize a much larger amount. Besides which, I have friends in the North who may come forward in the mean time to save me from ruin. Renew your bill at two months from to-day, and for those two months I will give you *double* the enormous interest I have been already paying – a ruinous bargain for me, and as valuable a one for you. But no favour; remember that! Do you accept?"

"I do," said Silas, after a few moments' deliberation. "The interest ought to be trebled, though."

The planter laughed bitterly.

"I have offered you the utmost farthing I mean to offer," he said.

"I accept it," answered Silas. "Give me pen, ink and paper, and I'll draw up the document."

CHAPTER IV.
CORA'S WELCOME.

SILAS CRAIG INTRODUCES HIS FRIEND BILL BOWEN

While the difficulties of the planter were becoming every day more painful to encounter, and more perilous to his future prospects of happiness, the good ship Virginia reached her destination, and in due time Mrs. Montresor and her two fair charges arrived at New Orleans.

Cora Leslie had given her father no warning of her coming. It had pleased the loving girl to think that she should creep to his side when he least expected her, and that the happy surprise of her arrival would come upon him in the midst of his troubles.

It was growing dusk on a lovely summer evening, when the travellers reached New Orleans. Bidding a hasty adieu to Adelaide Horton and Mrs. Montresor, with a promise to call upon them early the next day, Cora sprang into the carriage which Mortimer Percy had procured for her, requesting him to give the address to the driver.

"Your father is in town, Miss Leslie," said the young man. "You will have scarcely ten minutes' drive."

"Ten minutes!" cried Cora eagerly. "In ten minutes, then, I shall see my father!"

Her lovely countenance glowed with enthusiasm as she spoke; while her tiny hands were clasped in an ecstasy of delight.

Mortimer Percy's face grew strangely mournful as he looked upon the excited girl.

"One moment, Miss Leslie," he exclaimed earnestly, pausing, with his hand upon the carriage door. "You remember what I said to you in Grosvenor Square, on the night of my aunt's ball?"

"Yes, perfectly."

"You remember that I then told you I feared your father's welcome might not be so warm a one as your loving heart would lead you to desire. If to-night you should find it so, remember my warning, and do not doubt your father's affection, even should he receive you somewhat coldly. Remember, too, that come what may, and should the hour of trouble fall upon you, as it sometimes does on the youngest and the fairest; remember that you have always a friend in Mortimer Percy, and do not scruple to appeal to him."

He clasped her hand in his as he spoke, and she returned the friendly pressure.

"There is a mystery in your words which I seek in vain to fathom, Mr. Percy," she said; "and I know that your warnings fill me with a strange fear; but I know, too, that you have been very good to me, and should sorrow come, I will not hesitate to appeal to you and your cousin Adelaide."

"Adelaide is a good little girl," answered Mortimer, with a sigh; "but I shall be better able to serve you than she. Good night, Miss Leslie."

He released her slender hand, gave some directions to the driver, and in another moment the horse started, and Cora felt that she was on her way to her father's residence.

The sun was sinking in a bed of crimson glory, and the dusky shadows closing in the streets of New Orleans. The houses and public buildings were dimly visible in the declining light, as Cora looked out of the carriage window. The place seemed strange to her after her long residence in England. She had no memory of anything she saw, and felt that she was an utter stranger in her native land.

But she had not long to think of these things. The carriage drew up before her father's house, and the door was opened by the black servant, Caesar. Without waiting to ask any questions, she hurried into the hall, after dismissing the driver; but as she was about to inquire for her father, another negro servant emerged from one of the doors opening into the hall, and advanced to meet her.

He was past middle age. His hair was grizzled with patches of grey, and his face had an expression of settled melancholy rarely seen upon the negro countenance. He was dressed in a loose linen jacket and trousers, and his manner and appearance altogether denoted his station, which was that of confidential man and general servant, factotum to his master, Mr. Leslie.

This man's name was Toby. He had served the planter faithfully for five-and-twenty years.

"Mr. Leslie can see no one this evening," he said, as he approached Cora.

"He will not refuse to see me," murmured the young girl; "he cannot deny himself to his daughter."

"His daughter!" exclaimed the negro, with an irrepressible burst of enthusiasm; "his daughter, Miss Cora, that was away across the sea – yonder, in the free country. Cora, the child I used to nurse in the years that are gone by: ah, forgive me, forgive me, forgive the poor old negro slave, who is almost wild at the sight of his young mistress!"

The faithful creature fell on his knees at Cora's feet, and, clasping her hand in both his own, covered it with kisses.

"You remember me, then?" said Cora.

"I remember the little child that I used to carry in my arms, not the beautiful young lady from the happy English land; but the young lady has still the soft voice and the sweet smile of the little child, and she is not angry with poor Toby because he is beside himself with joy to see her once again."

"Angry with you!" exclaimed Cora; "but tell me, tell me, my father, where is he? Do not detain me longer when I should rush into his dear arms!"

"Your father—!" A sudden change came over the slave's manner. "Your father, Miss Cora! He thinks you still in the free English country, and when he hears that you have returned—" The negro paused, with an embarrassed countenance, as he uttered these words.

"What then?" cried Cora. "If I have returned without his knowledge, am I not his daughter; and who, in his hour of sorrow, has a better right to be at his side?"

"Yes, Miss Cora, but—"

"Tell me, where is he?"

"In that room, Miss Cora," answered the negro, gravely, pointing to the door of the study.

Without waiting for another word, Cora softly opened the door, and gliding into the room, stood for a moment mutely regarding her father. The Venetian shutters were closed, and a shaded lamp burned upon the planter's desk – a lamp that left the room in shadow, and threw its full light upon the careworn face of Gerald Leslie. The papers before him lay unheeded on his desk, with a half-burned cigar by their side. His finely moulded chin rested upon his hand, his brow was contracted by painful thoughts, and his dark brown eyes were fixed gloomily upon the ground.

He had not heard Cora's entrance. The young girl crept softly to his side, and dropping on her knees at his feet, clasped her hands about his left arm, which hung loosely over the arm of his chair.

"Father," she murmured, "dearest father!"

It was with no exclamation of joy, but with a cry of something nearer akin to agony, that the planter turned and beheld his only daughter.

"Cora!" he exclaimed; "Cora, *you* here!"

"Yes, dearest father. I know – I know that it is against your commands that I have come, but I felt that it could not be against your wishes."

Gerald Leslie's head dropped upon his breast with a gesture of despair.

"It needed but this," he murmured, "to complete my ruin."

These words were uttered in a voice so low as to escape the ear of Cora; but she could still perceive that her coming had not given her father the pleasure she had fondly hoped to have seen written in his face when he first beheld her.

"Father, father," she cried, piteously, clasping her arms about his neck, and gently drawing round his head, so as to be able to look in his face; "father, can it be that you do not love me?"

"*Not* love you, Cora, my darling, my darling!" Clasping his child to his breast, Gerald Leslie burst into a passion of sobs.

This was her welcome home.

* * * * * * *

Let us turn from the residence of Cora's father to the splendid mansion inhabited by the wealthy young planter, Augustus Horton, in one of the best streets of New Orleans.

It is upwards of a week after the arrival of Mrs. Montresor with her two fair charges. It is a bright summer morning, and the family party are assembled in an elegantly furnished apartment opening into a cool verandah filled with exotic plants. Mrs. Montresor, who, even in that warm climate, is too energetic to be idle, is seated at her embroidery. Her nephew, Augustus, lolls in an easy-chair, reading the New Orleans papers, while Adelaide Horton reclines in a hammock near the open window. Mortimer Percy, with his hands in the pockets of his light trousers, and a cigar in his mouth, leans against the window talking to his cousin.

"Say what you will, Mortimer, it is most extraordinary that Cora should not have called here since our return," exclaimed Adelaide.

"But do I not tell you, my dear cousin," answered the young man, "that Mr. Leslie has taken his daughter to his country seat upon the plantation?"

"What of that?" replied Adelaide. "Mr. Leslie's villa is but half an hour's drive from New Orleans. Nothing could have been easier than for him to have brought Cora here."

At this moment a female slave entered, announcing Mr. Craig.

"Show him in," said Augustus, without raising his eyes from the newspaper he was reading.

"Silas Craig!" exclaimed Mortimer, with a shudder of disgust. "What, in Heaven's name, induces you to encourage the acquaintance of that man, Augustus?"

"Pshaw, Mortimer, I have none of your romantic notions. Mr. Craig is a very respectable member of society."

"Respectable! Yes; the man who makes money is *respectable*, no matter by what shameful means he makes it. Usurer, oppressor of the helpless, trafficker in human flesh – what matters by what hideous trade the gold is got? The yellow guineas will not sparkle less – the hollow world will not be less ready to bow to the *respectable* member of society."

"Fool!" cried Augustus, angrily; "Craig is here. Do you wish him to know your opinion of him?"

Mortimer shrugged his shoulders and resumed his conversation with his cousin Adelaide.

Silas Craig saluted the ladies with ceremonious politeness, and, after the first greetings, exclaimed with a face expressive of sanctimonious grief and pious horror—

"Of course, ladies, you have heard the news?"

"The news! What news?" cried Adelaide and her aunt simultaneously.

"What! Is it possible that you have not heard of Mr. Gerald Leslie's conduct? All New Orleans is ringing with the scandal."

"What scandal?"

"Ah, ladies, you may indeed well ask what scandal; for who could believe that Mr. Leslie, one of the principal planters of Louisiana, should have been guilty of such a treason against the interests of society at large?"

"Treason! Mr. Leslie! What do you mean, Mr. Craig?" exclaimed Augustus Horton.

"I mean that Gerald Leslie has been discovered, within these last few days, to have educated in England the child of one of his slaves, a quadroon called Francilia, whom he sold to me some fourteen years ago. The girl has been brought up in England, where she has received the education of a princess, and it is only through her unexpected return to New Orleans that the secret has been discovered."

"Merciful Heaven!" cried Adelaide, hiding her face in her hands; "Cora a slave!"

"There was one spark of feeling at least," muttered Mortimer, as he watched his cousin's emotion.

"Now," pursued the pitiless usurer, "according to the Louisiana law, it is criminal to teach a slave to read. What, then, must be the offence of Mr. Leslie, in sending this girl to a first-class English boarding-school, and having her taught the accomplishments of a lady of the highest birth?"

"A terrible offence indeed, Mr. Craig," said Mortimer, bitterly; "but this girl is Gerald Leslie's own daughter, is she not?"

"She is; but what of that? Born of a slave mother, she is not the less his slave."

"I understand. As a worthy member of society, then, as a Christian and a gentleman – in the sense in which we regard these things – he may send his daughter to toil sixteen hours a day on his plantation; he may hand her to his overseer to be flogged, if she is too weak (or too lazy, as it will most likely be called) to work; he may sell her, if he will, no matter to what degradation – no matter to what infamy; but let him dare to *love* her – let him dare to look upon her with one thrill of fatherly affection – let him attempt to elevate her mind by education, to teach her that there is a free heaven above her, where slavery cannot be – let him do this, and he has committed a crime against society and the laws of Louisiana."

"Exactly so," replied Craig, rubbing his oily hands. "I see you understand the law of the land, Mr. Percy. No wonder that Gerald Leslie is a ruined man, he has wasted a princely income on the education of this girl – this slave."

"Poor Cora!" exclaimed Adelaide.

"What, Miss Horton, did you know her?" asked Craig.

"I did, indeed," replied Adelaide, "we were educated at the same school – we were bosom friends."

"Merciful Heaven!" exclaimed Craig, sanctimoniously; "to what pollution are our daughters exposed, when the children of slaves are foisted upon society in this manner!"

"No, Mr. Craig," cried Mortimer with a bitter laugh; "the pollution is in the very atmosphere of a clime in which a father's first duty to society is to trample on the laws of humanity – the ties of flesh and blood."

"Hold your tongue, Mortimer," said Augustus Horton, "you know nothing of these things; Gerald Leslie has acted disgracefully, and this girl must pay the penalty of her father's folly."

"That is Louisiana justice."

"Excuse me for two or three minutes, Mr. Craig," said Augustus, rising; "I have a few words to say to my cousin. I will rejoin you almost immediately; in the meantime the ladies will amuse you. Come, Mortimer."

The young man followed his cousin, after bowing coldly to Craig. The truth of the matter was that Augustus Horton wished to get his imprudent partner out of the way, as he felt that Silas Craig would take care to spread the report of Mortimer Percy's revolutionary principles amongst the outraged Southerners.

Left alone with the two ladies, Silas Craig felt himself very much at a loss for conversation.

He had never married, and he was always silent and ashamed in female society. Accomplished hypocrite as he was, he trembled before the keen instincts of a woman, and felt that his real nature stood unmasked.

But on this occasion he was relieved from his embarrassment in a manner he had little expected. Just as he was preparing himself to utter some commonplace remark, a stentorian voice resounded through the vestibule without.

"Oh, you needn't announce me," said the intruder; "everybody knows me. It's old Craig, the lawyer, I want to see, and I know he's here."

"A close observer might have noticed that Silas Craig's face grew considerably paler at the sound of his voice; but before he could make any remark, the owner of it had dashed into the room, banging open the door with a noise of thunder.

Well might the ladies start with an exclamation of amazement at the apparition that stood before them. The new comer was a tall, lanky, raw-boned looking man, with long hair, which streamed in rough locks from under his fur cap. He wore a bear-skin jacket, very much the worse for bad usage, loose knickerbocker trousers, leather gaiters, and great nailed boots; his red-striped shirt was torn and ragged, and a tattered cloak hung loosely over his shoulder. When we further add that he carried a musket under his arm, the reader will be able to understand the astonishment of Mrs. Montresor and her niece at beholding such an intruder in their elegant apartment.

If a ghost risen from the grave had stood before him, Silas Craig could scarcely have appeared more terrified than he did at the sight of this man.

"So I've found you at last, my worthy Craig, have I?" cried the stranger. "I've been over every inch of ground in New Orleans, I think, looking for you. At last somebody told me you were at Mr. Horton's.

'Very well, then,' says I, 'here goes for Mr. Horton's,' and here I am; but how is my dear Craig! You don't seem glad to see me."

"His dear Craig! Vulgar ruffian!" muttered Silas in an undertone; and then, with an effort to overcome his embarrassment, he said, "Why, as for being glad to see you, my dear Bill, of course, I'm glad; but you see – you see the truth was I thought you were in California."

"Yes, where you sent me to dig for gold and keep out of your way. No, the climate didn't agree with me, and I didn't find any gold, though I soon spent all I took with me. So, knowing I had powerful friends in New Orleans, I thought the best thing I could do would be to come back and throw myself once more on their generosity."

Silas Craig bit his thick under lip till the blood started beneath his teeth.

"But I say, Craig," said the stranger, looking at the two astonished women, "where's your manners? Ain't you going to introduce me to the ladies?"

"Oh, to be sure," replied Silas, with increasing embarrassment. "My dear Mrs. Montresor, my dear Miss Horton, allow me to introduce to you Mr. Bill Bowen, formerly captain of a slaver."

"Captain of a slaver!" exclaimed Adelaide.

"Don't be frightened, Miss," said Bill; "your brother was one of my best customers. I've done many a bit of business in the nigger trade with him."

The young girl shuddered as she turned away from the speaker.

"I know my dress ain't quite the thing for a lady's drawing-room," he said, looking down at his ragged shirt-sleeves and clay-stained clothes, "but we'll soon set all that to rights. My friend Craig will recommend me to his tailor and lend me the money to pay his bill, if it comes to that, won't you, Craig?"

"Oh, certainly, as far as that goes, in consideration for past services."

"Yes, 'in consideration for past services,' " repeated Bill Bowen, rather significantly. "I'll tell you what, Mr. Craig, as you seem doing the civil to these ladies here, and as you don't seem over much to relish my company, I'll slope now, and drop in and take a bit of dinner with you at your own house by-and-bye. What's your hour?"

"Six o'clock," muttered Craig, with ill-concealed vexation.

"Six o'clock. I shall be sure to be punctual," said Bill Bowen, "for I've got a pretty sharp appetite. Good morning, Ma'am. Good morning, Miss," he added, nodding familiarly to the two ladies, as he strode out of the room.

"What a horrible creature!" exclaimed Mrs. Montresor. "How can you tolerate him, Mr. Craig?"

"Why, the truth is," replied Silas, "the man has been of use to me in some trifling matters of business. He has served me for a long time one way and another, and I've got used to his queer ways. He's an eccentric sort of animal, and he works all the better for being humoured, so I look over his uncultivated manner."

"I would not advise you to encourage him in running after you into people's drawing-rooms," said Mrs. Montresor, pointing to the clay left by Bill Bowen's boot upon the rich colours of the Persian carpet.

Silas reddened, and an angry frown contracted his sandy eyebrows.

"I'll forgive him if he ever plays me this trick again," he muttered. "You are quite right, Mrs. Montresor, Mr. William Bowen requires to be taught a lesson, and I think Silas Craig is the man to teach it to him. Pray excuse the inconvenience you have been subjected to, and permit me to wish you a good morning."

"I cannot tell you how I dislike that man!" exclaimed Adelaide, when her aunt and she were alone; "he inspires me with a disgust for which I can scarcely account. And then, again, how cruelly he spoke of Cora! Poor girl, poor girl! a slave – a slave like Myra, or Daisy or Rose, or any of our servants. The friendship between us is broken for ever, and henceforth I dare not look upon her as my equal."

The iron hand of prejudice had so strangled every warmer emotion of the soul, that this girl, whose heart was naturally good and generous, was prepared to abandon for ever the friend and companion of her youth, because the taint of African blood was in her veins, the brand of society was stamped against her name – because she was a slave!

CHAPTER V.
PAUL LISIMON.

PAUL LISIMON READING THE GOSPEL IN THE NEGRO CABIN

We have now to retrace our steps; and, looking back at events which occurred some years before the opening of our story, introduce our readers to persons who are hitherto unknown to them.

Twenty years before the period of which we are writing, a certain wealthy Spaniard, calling himself Juan Moraquitos, came to New Orleans, and took up his abode in a superb villa residence, sufficiently removed from the din and bustle of the city, and yet commanding a view of the wide sweep of waters, and the dense forest of masts that thronged the quay. Amongst the scandal-mongers of New Orleans dark rumours were current on the first arrival of the haughty Spaniard. Whispers of terrible deeds done on the wide waste of waters; of piracy; carnage; murder, foul and secret, open and violent. But the dark stranger brought with him that which wins a welcome for the vilest – gold. None looked too closely to see the blood stains on the yellow coin. Don Juan Moraquitos was a great man in New Orleans before the year was out.

He brought with him a regiment of slaves, and a young wife, a pale, Spanish beauty with lustrous but melancholy eyes; eyes which loved to veil their soft radiance beneath long fringes of inky lashes; eyes in which the light of happiness was never seen to shine.

She was very lovely, Olympia Moraquitos, but those who looked on her sighed as they whispered to each other, that the Spaniard's pensive wife would have faded ere the lilies in her garden bloomed again.

It was so. Within six months of the arrival of Don Juan Moraquitos at New Orleans, the lovely Olympia slept in the cemetery on the north side of the city, leaving behind her an infant daughter, who had been christened Camillia.

An old female slave, who had followed her mistress from Don Juan's home in Mexico, whispered strange stories of the past. A forced marriage; tears; supplication; threats; long and patient agonies; a discarded lover and a broken heart. But whatever had been the history of the union between Juan Moraquitos and his young wife, none dared to breathe her name in the presence of the lonely widower. None could doubt that the haughty Spaniard had loved Olympia with a love as fathomless as jealous, and that the best treasures of his proud soul were buried in her grave.

But pride was even stronger than grief. Whatever anguish racked the solitary heart, the eagle eye was undimmed by a tear, the iron lip never quivered; no new wrinkles lined the arched brow, no premature weakness bowed the stalwart form. Don Juan Moraquitos was no common man.

It was nearly six years after the death of his wife before he noticed the helpless orphan she had left behind her. His first impulse was to banish the unhappy infant from his sight: the baby face too bitterly reminded him of her who was lost.

He had a small estate on the banks of the Mississippi; a lonely villa, half buried in the rich, tropical vegetation; its white walls gleaming from amidst a forest of emerald green, and wide sloping lawns that dipped into the deep blue water. It was a little paradise on earth.

Here Don Juan Moraquitos sent his infant daughter under the care of two women. The slave Pepita, who had nursed Olympia in her childhood and had attended her in her death-hour, and another female slave called Zara, a woman whose husband had been sold to a merchant of Florida, but who had been allowed to keep with her her son, an active negro boy of about six years old; these two women, with a couple of stout negro slaves, who worked in the gardens, composed the entire establishment of the baby heiress.

Time passed; the rosy lips began to form half articulate murmurs, then gentle and loving words. The baby learnt to speak her nurse's name, to prattle with the negro lad – Zara's son; to sing like some joyous bird as the little feet toddled hither and thither through the shady arcades of the garden.

Pepita, the infant's foster mother, loved the child with a wild and passionate devotion, rarely met with save in these simple half savage natures.

Zara attended to the household work, and waited on the nurse and her foster child. She was a woman of a reserved and taciturn temperament, and the warm-hearted Pepita felt repelled from any close intimacy by her stony manner.

It may have been that she brooded over the wrongs of a lifetime; it may have been that she remembered the day when her young husband had been torn from her arms and sold in the public market-place, as they sell a beast of burden.

As the baby Camillia grew into a laughing girl, the young negro loved to amuse the little heiress by indulging in all kinds of rough and impish gambols for her gratification. He sang to her; he danced before her; he made her toys from fragments of wood and coloured paper; he rigged a tiny vessel and set it afloat in a sheltered pool near the house; he was never tired of nursing her, nor of watching by her little cot as she slept.

Pepita, lazy like all negresses, was glad to have so much of the care of her young charge taken off her hands. She often left Tristan, the negro boy, to watch the slumbering child while she herself took a siesta in her rocking chair. It was exactly six years after the death of Olympia Moraquitos when the father's stern heart first melted to his orphan child. A sudden impulse took possession of him. In vain had he tried the distractions of the gaming-table, the theatre, commerce, dissipation, travel; none of these had been powerful enough to teach him to forget.

There was a void in his heart which nothing but a new affection could fill. He would see her. He would look once more upon the features which even in babyhood had recalled those of the dead. He would look on his child, even though the spirit of his lost Olympia seemed to rise from the grave and gaze at him out of the eyes of Camillia.

The little girl was asleep upon a grassy bank, half cradled in flowers, while the young Tristan kept watch a few paces from her side, when the dark form of Juan Moraquitos first threw its shadow across her pathway. She awoke at the sound of the Spaniard's footstep, and opening her large dark eyes, uttered a scream of terror.

The loneliness of her life had made the child timid as the young gazelle.

"You are not frightened of me, are you, Camillia?" said her father, laying his hand upon her silky, raven curls.

It was strange. As if subdued by an instinct, the girl lifted her dark eyes to his face, and answered quietly, "No."

"Yet you screamed when I first saw you?"

"Because you awoke me from my dream, and I thought you were the snake."

"The snake!" exclaimed Don Juan, "what snake?"

"I dreamt that I was in a beautiful garden; oh, much more beautiful even than this," said the child, "and I was very happy. The sun was shining, the birds singing, the river dancing in the light, as if it were glad of the joyous summer. But while I was thinking how beautiful the earth was, a black shadow came between me and the sunshine, and a horrible snake rose from the ground, and lifted itself – oh, ever so high above my head. That was why I screamed when I awoke."

Don Juan's brow darkened, and he could scarcely repress a shudder at the child's words.

"A strange dream," he murmured, "and a strange welcome for your father, Camillia."

"My father! are you my father?"

"Yes, little one."

"The grand gentleman that Pepita has told me of?"

"Yes, my Camillia. Will you love me?"

"I will try," answered the child, quietly.

It seemed, indeed, the shade of his departed Olympia that had returned to him in this lovely child. The same tinge of melancholy in the large, earnest black eyes; the same pale, lily tints in the complexion; the same slender and graceful form, telling of Andalusian extraction, and of the pure, purple blood that ran in the young veins.

Don Juan clasped his child to his breast in a transport of affection.

"My motherless darling!" he exclaimed— "my poor orphaned Camillia, to think that you and I should have been strangers so long! To think that my tiny blossom should have grown into so fair a flower, banished from its parent stem!"

The child's large wondering eyes were fixed upon her father's face, with a gaze of reverent awe.

"My mother!" she murmured; "my mother! Pepita says she is there."

She pointed as she spoke to the wide expanse of purple sky, melting into the deeper purple of the mighty river.

"Yes, my darling, she is in Heaven. From Heaven she looks down upon us and blesses us. Alas! poor child, she was not happy on earth!"

"Not happy! But had she not a garden like this, and beautiful singing birds and a fountain?"

"Yes, Camillia; she had all that wealth could purchase or art devise; yet she was not happy. But no more of this. Will you come with me, Camillia?"

"Where?"

"To a larger house than this – a place where there are gardens also, and the river – where you shall have play-fellows if you like."

All this time, Tristan, the negro boy, had been standing patiently in the background, beneath the shade of a superb magnolia.

"I have a playfellow here," said Camillia. "Tristan plays with me."

The brow of the haughty Spaniard contracted as he looked at the boy.

"Tristan is no fit playfellow for my little Camillia," he replied. "She must have companions of her own station. Tristan is a slave."

He took little pains to lower his voice as he said this. The young negro heard every word.

"A slave!" he muttered, as Don Juan led the child towards the house, and he was left alone in the gardens. "A slave!" Yes, I have been told that often enough. I must have heard it in my cradle, surely, when they sold my father as they sold their cattle, and put a brand on my arm as they mark their sheep, lest the animals should stray away or be stolen."

He pushed up the sleeve of his coloured calico shirt, and looked at his arm.

The two letters, J.M., had been branded on the flesh a little above the elbow.

Tristan stood motionless for some moments, looking earnestly at those two initials; then, bursting into a mocking laugh, he exclaimed—

"How clever they are! How powerful – how great! They can set their names upon our tortured flesh and mark *that* as their own; but they cannot brand our souls, slaves as we are; pitiful wretches as we may be, *those* are our own! Let them beware the hour when they come to learn the secret workings of those silent depths."

The boy walked slowly towards the house in the direction taken by Don Juan and his daughter.

A week after this, Camillia, the nurse, Pepita, Zara, and the boy, Tristan, were removed to the Villa Moraquitos in the suburbs of New Orleans.

The little girl was pleased by the change, and the two women were not sorry to bid farewell to the solitude of their old home for the gaiety of a city; but it was not so with Tristan; he was never tired of lamenting the luxuriant gardens in which he had played with his young mistress.

It was but seldom now that the negro lad saw Camillia. He was admitted now and then, it is true, to the splendid saloon looking out upon shaded verandahs, through which glimmered the broad expanse of the Mississippi. He was admitted sometimes to these costly rooms, in order to amuse the young heiress by his impish tricks, and his wild, half-demoniac songs; but Camillia was now under the care of a governess, a Frenchwoman, Mademoiselle Pauline Corsi, and this lady took no pleasure in the frolics of Tristan, whom she used to call *le diablin noir* (the little black devil).

Six months after the removal of Camillia and her little household to Villa Moraquitos, an event occurred which, for a brief space, disturbed the quiet monotony of the child's life.

It was in the depth of the brief South American winter when the brother-in-law of Don Juan Moraquitos arrived at the Villa.

This man was the only surviving relation of the Spaniard's dead wife, her elder brother, dearly beloved by her, but he who had forced upon her the marriage with his friend, Don Juan. His name was Tomaso Crivelli. He had come from Mexico on a tour through the United States, and had arrived at New Orleans – to die.

Yes; the hand of death was upon him. Fever had struck him down some days before. He was carried into Don Juan's house, and was in a state of delirium five hours after his arrival.

Three days after that he expired in the arms of his brother-in-law.

Half-an-hour before his death he became conscious, and implored Don Juan to send for an attorney. It was necessary that he should make a will.

The attorney sent for by the Spaniard was no other than Silas Craig, then thirteen years younger than at the commencement of our story.

The will was made, Don Juan and the attorney being the only witnesses to the signature, and a few minutes afterwards Don Tomaso Crivelli breathed his last, his hand locked in that of his brother-in-law, and his latest words a request to be buried by the side of his sister Olympia.

The funeral took place with the utmost pomp and splendour, and on the reading of the will it was found that Don Tomaso had left his entire fortune, consisting of a magnificent estate in Mexico, peopled by some hundreds of slaves, to his brother-in-law, Don Juan.

Thus was the Spaniard's immense wealth doubled by the addition of a fortune which he had no particular right to expect.

A marble mausoleum of wondrous beauty, with gates of sculptured bronze, was erected to contain the remains of Olympia and her brother; for the rich families of New Orleans never bury their dead below the earth, but each family has a vault wherein all its departed members are buried.

But Don Tomaso Crivelli had not come to Villa Moraquitos alone. He had brought a boy with him – a boy of about eight years of age, whom he called Paul.

This Paul was a handsome boy, with much of the Creole beauty in his appearance; none knew whence he came, or who he was. If any revelation was made by Don Tomaso, upon his death bed, respecting the lad; it was heard by no mortal ears but those of his brother-in-law, Don Juan, and he was silent now on the subject.

The boy was bitterly affected by the death of Don Tomaso. For days and weeks he shut himself up in the little chamber allotted to him, and refused to mix with the household.

Camillia was the only one from whom he would take comfort. When her little arms stole round his neck – when her childish voice murmured words of consolation into his ear, the sullen gloom of despair melted in a torrent of tears, and the boy flung himself upon the ground, and abandoned himself to a passion of grief.

This scene took place in the saloon occupied by Camillia and her governess, and in the presence of Don Juan, who spent some hours every day in his daughter's apartments.

"Let him weep," said the Spaniard; "poor boy, it will be best for him. I never saw such grief in one so young. Don Tomaso must have been very good to him."

"Good to me!" exclaimed Paul, springing from the ground; "he was indeed good. My father! my dear father! why have you left poor Paul for ever?"

"Your father!" said Don Juan, with an expression of astonishment.

"My dear, dear father!"

"My child, come hither," said the Spaniard, taking the boy's hand, and drawing him towards the sofa where he was seated. "You call my departed relative your father. Were you in the habit of addressing him thus?"

"Yes, always."

The Spaniard smiled gravely.

"Your patron was very good to you," he said, "and no doubt, in his affection for you, it pleased him to hear you call him father; but, of course, you knew that you were not really his son."

"Not his son!"

"No. Tell me, what is your name?"

"In Mexico they always called me Paul."

"Yes, but Paul is your Christian name. Did they call you by no other name – no surname?"

"There were several negroes called Paul, and sometimes, when they wanted to name me from the slaves, they called me Paul Lisimon."

"Good; then Lisimon is your name. Do you remember your mother?"

"No; I have heard them say that she died when I was a baby."

"And with whom have you been all your life?"

"Always with my father – Don Tomaso."

A crimson flush mounted to the boy's pale brow as he spoke. It seemed as if a bitter feeling of shame and anguish came over him at the thought that he whom he had so dearly loved was his superior, his patron, but not his father.

"Do not fear, my child," said Don Juan, laying his hand upon the boy's curling hair; "do not fear for the future. My brother loved you, that is sufficient for me: this house will be your home. I will charge myself with your education, and with your fate in life. All that he could have been to you I will be."

"Not all, not all," answered Paul naively; "I can never love you as I loved him."

* * * * * * * *

Don Juan Moraquitos kept his word. Paul Lisimon was brought up in the household of the Spaniard.

For the first few years his education was entrusted to the care of Mademoiselle Pauline Corsi, and Paul and Camillia learned the same lessons side by side. When the lad reached the age of fourteen a tutor was engaged, who came to Villa Moraquitos for two hours every day, to teach the boy Latin, Greek, and mathematics. It was Don Juan's intention to make his *protégé* a lawyer, and Paul's beautiful intellect and energetic nature gave promise of a brilliant career in whatever profession might be chosen for him.

The slaves upon the Spaniard's noble estate had a strange love for this boy – a reverent and admiring affection, such as simple natures can feel for one whom they look up to as a superior being. The dark faces would brighten when Paul Lisimon appeared on the plantation, amidst the little village of huts inhabited by the negroes.

It was the chief delight of the boy's leisure hours to visit and instruct these people.

He beheld in them simple but noble natures, obscured by the dark veil of ignorance. Enthusiastic and hopeful, the young student looked forward to a day when, from the ranks of these despised people, great men should arise to elevate the African race, and to declare aloud in the Senate, and before the assembled nations, the EQUAL RIGHTS OF THE GREAT BROTHERHOOD OF MAN.

Often, of a winter's night, the boy Paul might have been seen seated opposite to the glowing wood fire in one of the huts reading aloud to a grey headed negro and his wife the eloquent pages of Holy Writ.

How eagerly the simple creatures listened to the sacred words; how gladly their weary ears drank in the blessed sound; how readily their dull eyes opened to the light of the Gospel! Paul Lisimon, boy as he was, knew that even more precious than education is religion; and his first care was to teach them to remember a Creator who was mightier than any earthly master, and Who could, if it was His merciful will, release them from all their bonds, and set them free in a land of glory.

Thus passed the boyhood of the orphan lad, Paul Lisimon.

Often when the moonbeams bathed the sleeping city in their effulgent glory; when the mighty Mississippi seemed a tide of molten silver; often in the stillness of a summers night, Paul Lisimon knelt beside the stately sepulchre in which Don Tomaso Crivelli lay. "My father!" exclaimed the boy, clasping his lifted hands; "for if thou wert not indeed my father, thou wert still dearer than the best of fathers to me. Sleep in peace, noble soul! the creature of thy bounty remembers and cherishes thine image. Never will he be unworthy of the love thou gavest him. Never will he be untrue to the teaching of his infancy."

CHAPTER VI.
THE LAWYER'S MAP OF THE UNITED STATES.

Bill Bowen, the slave-dealer, kept his appointment, and at six o'clock precisely presented himself at the house of Silas Craig, the attorney.

His host did his best to conceal the disgust he felt at having to entertain the worthy Mr. Bowen.

An excellent dinner was served by a female slave, whose peculiarly hideous appearance had obtained for her the name of Venus.

The civilized and educated owners of these poor creatures love their joke, and it is not to be expected that they should remember that even an African may possibly have *feelings* – feelings that may be wounded by sneers and cruel jests, as the slave's back is scored by the gaoler's whip.

After dinner – at which meal Mr. Bowen did such execution as to clear every dish set before him, and to empty his glass as often as his host would fill it – Silas and his visitor retired to the lawyer's private office, where claret, Jackson punch, gin sling, sherry cobbler, and other American beverages were set out upon a sideboard adorned with ice pails, while the small office table had been cleared of its papers and covered with fruit and glasses.

"Well done, governor! I like the look of this," said the free and easy Mr. Bowen, as he seated himself in a rocking chair, and producing a short stick, whittled away perseveringly. "This looks like business; this looks like making a night of it."

Most men would have been considerably elevated, if not frightfully intoxicated, with the amount of wine that Bill Bowen had already drunk. Not so that gentleman; he was as cool and collected as if he had been only taking so much water.

Silas Craig turned the key in the door of the apartment before he seated himself.

"Why have you done that?" asked Bowen.

"Because, as our conversation will most likely be of a private and confidential nature, I wish to guard against being disturbed."

"You always was a cunning one, governor," said Bill approvingly, as he poured himself out an immense bumper of claret, which he tossed off at a draught.

"And now that we are alone, my dear Bowen," continued Silas, in a tone that was meant to be very affectionate, "pray may I ask what has brought you to New Orleans?"

"What!" exclaimed Bowen. "Shall I tell you what, governor? Empty pockets and an empty stomach. Look at these here," he added, pointing to his ragged trousers and rough jacket, which he had not changed since the morning. "These don't look much like prosperity – do they?"

"They are a little the worse for wear, certainly, my dear Bowen; but you were always eccentric, and may be allowed to choose your own costume."

"Then I'd rather choose one that'll keep the weather out a little better than this," growled Bill.

"To be sure, to be sure; but what do you want of *me*?"

"What do I want! Why, what do you suppose I want? It isn't fine speeches; no, nor yet good dinners – though you certainly have given me a jolly good feed – that will satisfy me. I want money."

"Hum! How much, my dear William?" asked the lawyer, rubbing his chin, thoughtfully.

"A thousand dollars."

"My dear friend, my impetuous William, you must certainly be joking," answered Silas, blandly; "you surely do not forget that it is only a twelvemonth since you received that sum, for which I have your acknowledgment in my desk yonder, signed and dated."

"Dated!" exclaimed Bowen; "as far as that goes, I don't think we're either of us likely to forget the date, seein' as it was dated the day after Gerald Leslie's partner, Philip Treverton, *died*!"

A faint shade of pallor crept over the face of Silas Craig as Bowen uttered these words.

"You will remember," he said, "that at the time of your giving me that acknowledgment, it was an understood thing that you were to expect nothing more from me."

"Perhaps it was, and perhaps it wasn't," answered Bowen; "but I've had time for serious reflection in the last twelvemonth, and I've come to the conclusion that I wasn't fairly paid for my share in the transaction."

"Hush! moderate your voice, my dear William: remember, walls have ears."

"I don't care for that. I say I wasn't fairly paid. Look at what you made by the business!"

"My dear William!"

"I'll tell you what, governor, if you don't want me to talk loud, you'd better give me a thousand-dollar bill before I'm riz; for when my back's once up I can't answer for myself easy, and I may be letting some of your niggers into our little secrets before I know where I am; and niggers is good uns to talk, as you know."

"Come, come, my dear Bowen, don't excite yourself," said Silas, soothingly; "you shall have the money."

"Yes, I mean to; but when?"

"Before you leave this house to-night."

"Well, I guess I don't mean to leave without it. Now, you just look here: what's the story as the New Orleans folks tells of Mr. Treverton's death?"

"I scarcely know."

"Oh, yes, you do; you know every word of it, for it was you who set it afloat. They say as Mr. Treverton, having lost a large sum of money at *rouge et noir*, was unable to pay all his losses, and was insulted by a young Frenchman, a stranger in New Orleans. A duel, or rather an assassination, took place on the spot. Phillip Treverton was stabbed to the heart, and the Frenchman and a party of his friends made off, carrying the body of the murdered man with them. A fortnight afterwards the body was found in the Mississippi: decomposition had taken place, and the face was not to be recognized, but from cards and papers found in the pockets, the corpse was known to be that of Treverton: it was therefore buried in the Treverton vault. The police set to work to discover the particulars of the assassination, and, if possible, to find the murderer; they failed in both attempts, as *you* know. The Government seal was set on the effects of the deceased, which were examined by Gerald Leslie on his return from Europe. That for which Leslie looked most anxiously amongst his late partner's papers was a certain document, the receipt for one hundred thousand dollars, paid to Mr. Silas Craig, attorney and money-lender. *He did not find it.*"

William Bowen walked over to the sideboard, and helped himself to a tumbler of Jackson punch.

"My dear friend, why recur to these things? They belong to the past."

"Perhaps they do; but as I want that money, I thought I might as well touch up your memory a little bit, governor." ·

"You shall have the money, William; you shall have the money. I suppose, when you've got it, you'll be leaving New Orleans again?"

Mr. William Bowen laughed aloud.

"That's what you'd like, ain't it, Mr. Craig? You'd rather have my room than my company, I guess; but Lor' bless you, I know when I'm well off as soon as any one. I shall take up my quarters in this here city, and I look to you to find me a comfortable situation. I can turn my hand to a many things, as you know, and I ain't proud."

"Well, well, my dear William, we'll do our best."

"I knew you would, governor. You're too clever to quarrel with your friends, and you can't afford to quarrel with me."

Having emptied his tumbler of punch, Mr. Bowen flung himself back in his rocking chair, and, with his hob-nailed boots and knickerbockers elevated considerably above his head, swung himself backwards and forwards.

As he did so his face was turned away from Silas Craig, and that gentleman regarded Mr. Bowen with a look of aversion which rendered the attorney's countenance even more repulsive than usual.

"Curse him!" muttered Silas, as he watched William Bowen rocking himself to and fro, and chewing an immense lump of tobacco. "Curse him! why didn't he kill himself with drink, or get a bowie-knife through his heart in some drunken Californian row?"

Why not, indeed, Mr. Silas Craig? It is sometimes very difficult to get rid of the instruments of crime. The murderer who intruded at Macbeth's banquet, with blood upon his face, was scarcely welcome at that festivity; but the Scottish monarch was a criminal, and he was no longer his own master. He had become the slave of GUILT.

The attorney's private office was a large and roomy apartment, handsomely but plainly furnished with desks, cabinets, japan cases, filled, no doubt, with valuable documents, securely padlocked, and inscribed with the names of different clients. The floor was spread with India matting, and the room was lighted by gas lamps, whose glaring brilliancy was softened by green shades. The only noticeable piece of furniture in the apartment was a large painted map of the United States, which was fixed against the wall opposite to Mr. Bowen.

This map was surrounded by rather a massive framework of polished ebony, handsomely carved in a floreated pattern, and ornamented on each side with the arms of America.

As Mr. William Bowen rocked backwards and forwards, chewing tobacco and staring straight before him, his eyes were necessarily fixed upon this map. A strange, sinister smile came over his face as he contemplated it.

"You make frequent use of that there map of your'n, don't you governor?" he said.

"No, no, my dear William, not such very frequent use," answered Silas.

"Oh yes, but you do now. Come, don't try on any gammon with me, because it won't do, governor. How are your clients?"

"Which clients?"

"Your lambs – your poor little pigeons"

"My pigeons!"

"Yes, Mr. Innocent. Your pigeons in Columbia Street – the poor little pigeons that drop in every night to lose their money in a certain mysterious house which the police would like to know more about. Come, governor, it's all very well to keep up the farce with the worthy citizens of New Orleans; it's all very well to show your sanctified countenance in church and at meeting. *They* may be taken in, but *I* can't, and you know it. We've worked together, and there ain't many secrets between us. Let's have a look at 'em next door."

Silas Craig bit his under lip with ill-concealed vexation; but this man had evidently some power over the money-lending attorney. He shrugged his shoulders, and rising from his seat, went over to the map of the United States.

"Come then," he said; "I can't refuse you anything, my dear William."

As he said this he touched a projecting portion of the carved escutcheon representing the arms of Columbia.

The map slid softly to one side of the framework, leaving an aperture the size of a small doorway.

On the other side of this aperture there was nothing to be seen but a dark and narrow passage.

Silas and Bowen entered this passage, the former taking care to replace the sliding panel as he did so.

"You know the way," whispered the attorney; "follow me. Walk quietly if you can, and keep those cursed boots of yours from creaking."

The two men crept softly along the dark passage, which was not wide enough to admit of two walking abreast. This narrow corridor was full two hundred yards long. It ran the whole length of a block of houses, and communicated with a dwelling in a street running parallel with that in which the attorney's house was situated.

This narrow passage, therefore, connected two houses in two separate streets – houses which had apparently no connection whatever.

There were many secrets in the history of Silas Craig's immense wealth, and this was one of them.

A faint light glimmered at the extreme end of the dark passage – a light which seemed at first no larger than a pin's point, but which, as the two men approached nearer to it, extended itself into a small oval patch of radiance.

This patch of light proceeded from a tiny glass window, such as that inserted in the door of a private box in an opera-house or theatre.

Silas and Bowen looked through this tiny window into the apartment with which it communicated.

A strange scene met their eyes.

The apartment into which they looked was an immense saloon, devoted to the infernal sport of the gambler.

The immense green-cloth-covered table was scattered with cards, and ornamented with the complicated machinery necessary for the game of roulette.

The rake of the croupier was constantly busy, drawing the stakes into the coffers of the bank; but there was no chinking of dollars, no flash of silver, no gleam of yellow gold.

The gamblers of New Orleans played for no such insignificant stakes. A pile of notes lay at the left hand of each player; a pile of notes, the lowest of which was for five dollars, while many of the oblong fragments of tissue paper represented fifties and hundreds. There were no exclamations, no oaths, no laughter, no animation. There was the solemn calm of men whose very lives are staked upon the venture; the awful silence of men whose inmost souls revolve with every turn of the fatal wheel.

There were men there whose vast riches were melting nightly away, but who could no more resist the terrible fascination of play than they could transform their natures. There were those who staked the money of others upon the green cloth of that fatal table – honourable men, perhaps, heretofore, but given over to the gambler's madness, and powerless to resist the fiend. There were husbands and fathers who had beggared a beloved wife and children, who had seen the loving partners of their life fade day by day, who had heard the feeble cries of helpless infants asking for bread, but who still played on, as if Satan himself had been standing at their elbow to urge them to destruction.

At this scene of horror, at this hell upon earth, Silas Craig, the usurer, gazed with a chuckle of delight and triumph.

"Play away, fools!" he muttered, "play away. Lose your money, and go and drown yourselves in the Mississippi afterwards. The citizens of New Orleans little think, when they bring their dollars to the house in Columbia Street, that Silas Craig is the gainer by their want of brains."

CHAPTER VII.
PRIDE OF CASTE.

Nearly a month had elapsed since the arrival of the Virginia in the harbour of New Orleans, and still Adelaide Horton and Cora Leslie had not met.

The young Creole, generous-hearted as she was, had never felt the same affection for her old schoolfellow since the fatal revelation made by Silas Craig. It was in vain that the generosity of her nature would have combated with the prejudices of her education; pride of caste was the stronger, and she could not but despise Cora, the lovely descendant of slaves. In the meantime the two girls had ceased to meet. The nature of Adelaide Horton was capricious and volatile, and, in a few days, she had almost dismissed Cora's image from her memory.

Indolent, like all Creoles, Adelaide spent the greater part of her days in a rocking-chair, reading a novel, while fanned by her favourite slave, Myra. Mortimer Percy was, as we know, by no means the most attentive of lovers, although living in the same house as that occupied by his fair cousin. He saw her but seldom, and then evinced an indifference and listlessness which often wounded the volatile girl.

"How weary and careless he is," she thought; "how different to Gilbert Margrave, the artist, the poet, the enthusiast!"

Alas, Adelaide, beware of that love which is given without return! Beware of the bitter humiliation of finding that he whom you have secretly admired and reverenced – he whose image you have set upon the altar of your heart, and have worshipped in the sanctity of silence and of dreaming – that even he, the idol, the beloved, looks on you with indifference, while another usurps the earnest devotion of his poet soul.

Adelaide Horton had ample time for indulgence in those waking dreams which are often so dangerous. A school-girl, young, romantic and frivolous, ignorant of the harsh ways of the world, she built fair castles in the air – ideal palaces in a lovely dreamland, which were only too soon to be shattered to the ground.

Gilbert Margrave came to New Orleans armed with those brilliant schemes of inventions in machinery, which might, as he fondly hoped, supersede slave labour, though not militating against the employment of the many.

He came well furnished with letters of introduction from powerful men in England, to planters and merchants of New Orleans; but though he met with much politeness and hospitality, the Louisianians shrugged their shoulders and shook their heads when he revealed his opinions and tried to win their approval of his plans. They looked upon the handsome young engineer with a feeling something akin to pity. He was an enthusiast, and, like all enthusiasts, no doubt a little of a madman.

One of the first houses at which Gilbert Margrave presented himself, was that of Augustus Horton. He found Adelaide and her aunt alone in their favourite morning room; one lounging in her rocking-chair, the other, as usual, busy at an embroidery frame.

The young Creole looked very pretty in her loose and floating morning robe of India muslin, richly trimmed with Valenciennes lace, and peach-coloured ribbons. Her hair was arranged in clusters of short ringlets, which trembled in the summer breeze, wafted in through the Venetian blinds of the verandah.

As the name of Gilbert Margrave was announced, the animated girl sprang from her easy chair, and, flinging down her book, ran forward to receive the long-looked for visitor.

"At last!" she exclaimed. "I was sure you would come, but I have looked out for you so anxiously – I mean we all have," she added, blushing.

"A thousand thanks for your kind welcome, Miss Horton. Believe me, your house is one of the very first to which I have directed my steps."

"How good of you to remember us."

"Say, rather, how selfish," replied Gilbert. "Do you think it is no happiness, in a foreign country, to find one circle at least where one is not a stranger?"

"Nay, Mr. Margrave," said Mrs. Montresor; "will you not call us a circle of friends?"

"But pray sit down," exclaimed Adelaide, pointing to a low chair, near a stand of perfumed exotics in one of the windows, "sit down and tell us all your adventures by land and sea, especially the latter, and how you have survived the hair-breadth 'scapes and ventures of the briny Atlantic."

Gilbert Margrave told, in a few words, the particulars of his voyage, which had been a rapid and pleasant one; "So rapid a passage," he continued with a smile, "that I trust I am yet in time to assist at the wedding of Miss Horton and my old friend Mortimer Percy."

A shade of vexation crossed Adelaide's pretty face.

"I really do not see," she said, "why all the world should be in such a hurry for this marriage. There is surely time enough. One would think I was in danger of becoming an old maid, or else that everybody was desirous of getting rid of me."

"I do not think there is much fear of either contingency," replied Gilbert, laughing.

"The truth is, Mr. Margrave," said Mrs. Montresor, "that my dear Adelaide is a spoiled child, and because her cousin happens to be a very sensible, high-principled young man, but not exactly a hero of romance, she thinks herself called upon to affect a contempt for him. But I know her better than she knows herself, and I am certain that, at the bottom of her heart, she cherishes a very sincere affection for Mortimer."

"How can you know what's at the bottom of my heart, when I don't know myself, aunt Lucy?" exclaimed Adelaide, impatiently; "upon my word, I think no girl was ever so cruelly used as I have been. Other people make up a marriage for me, other people tell me whom I love, when I ought to know a deal better than they do. It's really shameful!"

If the real cause of Adelaide's indignation could have been known, it would have been discovered that her anger was not so much aroused against her aunt as against Gilbert Margrave, for the indifferent manner in which he had spoken of her approaching marriage.

Anxious to quell the storm, of which he little knew himself to be the cause, the young engineer endeavoured to turn the conversation, and in order to do so, he asked a question which had been trembling on his lips from the very first.

"Your friend, Miss Leslie," he said: "the star of your farewell assembly – you often see her, I suppose, Miss Horton?"

Gilbert Margrave little knew that this very question only added fuel to the fire already raging in the breast of the impetuous girl.

"I have never seen Cora Leslie since our arrival in New Orleans," she answered, coldly.

"Indeed! But I thought you such intimate friends. Miss Leslie – she is not ill, I hope?"

His evident anxiety about Cora terribly irritated Adelaide Horton.

"That question I cannot answer. I know nothing whatever of Miss Leslie; for, I repeat, we have not met since we reached America."

"May I ask why this is so, Miss Horton?"

"Because Cora Leslie is no fit associate for the daughter of Edward Horton."

The blood rushed in a crimson torrent to the face of the young engineer. He started from his seat as if he had been shot.

"In Heaven's name, Miss Horton," he exclaimed, "what would you insinuate; surely nothing against the honour of—"

"I insinuate nothing, Mr. Margrave," answered Adelaide. "I simply tell you that the – the person of whom you speak is no companion for me. Whatever friendship once existed between us is henceforth forever at an end – Cora Leslie is a slave!"

A choking sensation had risen to the throat of the young engineer during this speech. Unutterable anguish had possessed him at the thought that he was perhaps about to hear of some stain upon the character of Cora. What, then, was his relief at finding how much he had wronged her purity, even by that fear?

"A slave!" he replied.

"Yes; African blood flows in her veins. She has never been emancipated; she is, therefore, as much a slave as the negroes upon her father's plantation."

"I was led to believe something to this effect on the very night of your aunt's ball in Grosvenor Square, Miss Horton. So far from this circumstance lessening my respect for Miss Leslie, I feel that it is rather exalted thereby into a sentiment of reverence. She is no longer simply a beautiful woman; she henceforth becomes the lovely representative of an oppressed people."

"Your opinions are rather Quixotic, Mr. Margrave," replied Adelaide, with a sneer; "and I fear you will find yourself almost in as painful a position as the Spanish knight if you venture to make them known in New Orleans."

"Whatever danger I may incur of being either ridiculed or persecuted, I shall never conceal my detestation of prejudice and tyranny, and my sympathy with the weak," answered Gilbert proudly. "Pardon me, if I speak warmly on this subject, Miss Horton; it is not to be supposed that you and I should think alike. We represent the opposite sides of the Atlantic."

"Nay, Mr. Margrave," replied Adelaide, whose brief outburst of anger had passed like a thunder cloud in a sunny sky, "it is I who should ask pardon. I fear I am a passionate and heartless creature, but I cannot help feeling some indignation against Mr. Leslie for the cheat he has put on us."

Adelaide Horton scarcely dared own to herself that it was jealousy of Gilbert's evident partiality for Cora, rather than anger against the young girl herself, that had been the cause of her cruel words.

Augustus Horton entered the room at this moment, and Adelaide presented her brother to the young engineer.

There was little sympathy between Gilbert Margrave and the planter of New Orleans. Augustus had never quitted the Southern

States, except on the occasion of one or two brief visits to New York. His ideas were narrow, his prejudices deeply rooted. He was by no means free from the vices of his fellow-citizens; he was known to frequent the gambling houses, which, in spite of the law promulgated for their suppression, still existed in New Orleans; but he was known, also, to be prudent, even in the midst of his dissipation, and never to have jeopardised the splendid estate left him by his father.

But hospitality is an universal virtue with the Creoles, and Augustus bade the young engineer a hearty welcome to his house.

They conversed for some time on indifferent subjects, and Gilbert, having accepted an invitation to dinner for the following day, was about to take his leave, when he was prevented by the entrance of the slave, Myra.

The girl approached her mistress with an embarrassed manner unusual to her.

"What is the matter with you, Myra?" asked Augustus, impatiently. "What are you standing there for? Why don't you speak?"

"Oh, if you please, massa," stammered the girl, "there is a young person below who asks to see my mistress, and who calls herself Miss Leslie."

"Gerald Leslie's daughter here!" exclaimed Augustus. "This is too much. This is what her father exposes us to in not teaching this girl her real position."

"What is to be done?" asked Adelaide, turning pale.

"Can you ask?" replied her brother. "Surely there is but one course. I will ask Myra here," he added, pointing to the young Quadroon. "Tell me, girl, what do you think of this young person?"

"Why, massa, I – I – thought that in spite of the whiteness of her skin, she must be—"

"Of the same rank as yourself; is it not so?"

"Yes, massa."

"Very well, then; do you think it possible that your mistress could receive her as a visitor – as an equal?"

"Oh no, massa!" exclaimed the girl.

"That is enough. You can let her know this."

Myra curtsied, and was about to leave the room when Gilbert Margrave arrested her by an imperious motion of his hand.

"Stay!" he exclaimed. "Pardon me, Mr. Horton, if I presume to say that this must not be. I had the honour of meeting Miss Leslie one evening at the house of your aunt. Permit me, therefore, to spare her an insult which I should feel myself a dastard in tolerating. Allow me to carry your answer to Miss Leslie?"

"You, sir!" exclaimed Augustus Horton.

"Oh, pardon me, Mr. Horton, if I appear to make a bad return for the kind welcome you were so ready to offer to a stranger; but remember that the customs and prejudices of the South are new to me, and forgive me if I say that the conduct which on your part would only be natural, would become on mine an abominable cowardice!"

"Sir!" cried the indignant Augustus.

Before he could say more, Gilbert Margrave bowed deferentially to the ladies, and to the angry planter himself.

"Oh, it is too clear – he loves her!" exclaimed Adelaide, when they were alone.

"And even if he does," said her aunt, quietly; "what difference can it possibly make to Miss Adelaide Horton that is – Mrs. Mortimer Percy that is to be?"

Crimson mounted to Adelaide's face at this remark. She made no answer, but with an angry look at her aunt, hurried from the room.

This display of emotion had not escaped the penetrating eye of her brother.

"What is the meaning of this, my dear aunt?" he asked.

"I very much fear, Augustus, that your sister has no great inclination to marry her cousin, Mortimer Percy."

"And the cause of this disinclination is some foolish preference for the insolent European who has just left us?"

"Unhappily, yes."

"This is too humiliating," exclaimed Augustus, walking rapidly up and down the apartment; "my sister degrades herself by evincing a marked predilection for a man who is indifferent to her, and the object of her admiration does her the honour to prefer a – slave!"

CHAPTER VIII.
TOBY TELLS THE STORY OF THE MURDERED FRANCILIA.

THE MULATTO REVEALS THE FATAL SECRET

On an elevated terrace, fifty feet above the margin of a lake, was situated the summer pavilion occupied by the once wealthy planter, Gerald Leslie.

Thick shrubberies of magnolia and arbutus, intersected by winding pathways, and varied by rockeries, lay between the terrace and the limpid waters below. Tall palms spread their feathery branches above the roof of the pavilion, and exotic flowers bloomed beneath the colonnade of bamboo work which surrounded the light edifice. A flight of marble steps led from the glass door of the pavilion, and a balustrade of the same pure white material stretched the whole length of the terrace, at each end of which were sculptured marble vases, filled with the rarest blossoms. A flower garden, in exquisite order, surrounded the pavilion, while exactly opposite the verandah, a rustic table and some garden chairs were placed beneath the luxuriant shade of a banana tree.

Seated on the steps leading from the pavilion, faithful as a dog who listens for the footsteps of his beloved master, the slave Toby might have been seen on the day following that on which Cora had paid her unwelcome visit at the house of Augustus Horton.

Gerald Leslie was at his office in New Orleans, where business often detained him when the best wishes of his heart would have kept him by his daughter's side.

The summer afternoon was hot and sultry, and all the windows were open. The slave seemed to be listening eagerly for some sound within.

"All is silent," he said, sorrowfully; "that pretty bird sings no more. What has happened? Something, I know. I saw by her sad face when she returned from New Orleans yesterday, that all was not well with the sweet young mistress. The sorrows of those he loves cannot escape the eyes of poor Toby."

At this moment a light footstep sounded behind him, and Cora Leslie emerged from the pavilion.

The young girl was dressed in the thinnest white muslin, which floated round her graceful figure, aerial as some vapoury cloud in the summer sky. She was pale, and a mournful shadow dimmed the orient splendour of her large black eyes. She descended the marble steps slowly, without perceiving the faithful slave who had risen at her approach, and who stood aside regarding her earnestly.

"Miss Cora is sad," he said presently; "will she forgive the poor slave if he presumes to ask why?"

She started at the sound of the mulatto's voice, and turning towards him held out her hand silently.

Toby took the little hand in his and raised it to his lips.

"Miss Cora does not deny that she is sad," he repeated.

"Not so much sad, Toby, as bewildered," replied the young girl. "My reception at the house of my old school-fellow has filled my mind with perplexity. What could be the meaning of Adelaide Horton's conduct?"

"Forgive me, Miss Cora, if I remind you that your father particularly requested you not to leave the house during his absence."

"I know, Toby, I know. But why that request? Why am I a prisoner here? Why is my father's manner more indicative of sorrow than joy at my return to Louisiana? Why, on my first visit to the friend of my youth, do I find the door shut in my face?"

"But the English gentleman who conducted you home explained the reason of that, Miss Cora?"

"No, Toby; Mr. Margrave endeavoured to explain, but in doing so he only revealed his embarrassment. There is some secret in all this. Some mystery that— Hark!"

The sound which arrested Cora's attention was the trampling of a horse's hoofs upon the carriage drive below the terrace.

"Hulloa!" cried a voice from the same direction. "Hulloa, there! Is there any one to hold my horse?"

"A visitor!" exclaimed Cora.

"It is Mr. Augustus Horton," said Toby, looking over the balustrade.

"Adelaide's brother! Then I will see him."

"But in your father's absence, Miss Cora?" murmured the slave, anxiously.

"I will see him," repeated Cora; "he may come to offer an explanation – Heaven knows it is needed."

"Hulloa! every one asleep here?" cried the voice below.

"Coming, massa," answered Toby, running down the terrace steps.

Three minutes afterwards Augustus Horton made his appearance in the flower-garden, where Cora awaited him. He bowed carelessly to the young girl without raising his hat, but fixing upon her lovely face a gaze of ardent admiration.

He carried a light riding-whip in his hand, and was smoking a cigar, which he did not remove from his mouth.

"Miss Cora Leslie, I presume?" he said.

Cora bowed.

"Mr. Leslie is not at home, I understand?"

"I am expecting his return, at any moment, Mr. Horton," answered Cora.

Something in the planter's familiar manner, and in his ardent gaze filled the young girl with indignant surprise, and she looked at him with a glance of astonishment as he flung a sealed packet upon the table, and seated himself, without invitation, in one of the rustic chairs.

"I have some papers to restore to your father," he said; "but that is not the whole object of my visit. My sister told me that you were lovely, Miss Leslie, but I now perceive that in such a case a woman never tells more than half the truth."

Cora had remained standing during this speech. She now seated herself in the chair opposite to that taken by the young planter, and said, calmly,–

"Pardon me, Mr. Horton, but I imagined that the object of your visit here—"

"Was to reply to the letter addressed by you to my sister, Adelaide? Yes, Miss Leslie, that letter proved to us that Mr. Margrave had not properly acquitted himself of the commission which he undertook."

"How so, sir?"

"My sister much regretted not being able to receive you, yesterday, and I should have shared those regrets, had she not chosen me to bring you her excuses."

"It is not an excuse which I require, Mr. Horton, but an explanation," replied Cora, with dignity.

Augustus shrugged his shoulders.

"What further explanation can you require, Miss Leslie," he said; "the preparations of her approaching marriage? A little touch of headache, perhaps. Is not this sufficient to explain all?"

"No, sir, it is not. Because I would rather hear the truth, bitter as that truth may be, than these courteous mockeries which put me to the rack. Mr. Percy's opposition to my return to America; my father's emotion on beholding me; the strange isolation in which I am kept; and lastly, your sister's extraordinary conduct of yesterday – all these prove to me that some terrible fatality overshadows me; a fatality of which I am ignorant, but which I am determined to discover."

"Nay, Miss Leslie, what is that you would seek to know? why not be content to reign by your grace and beauty? for the fatality of which you speak can cast no cloud upon your loveliness; and even the jealousy of our wives and sisters cannot rob you of your sovereignty."

"I do not understand you, sir."

"And yet I endeavoured to make myself understood. Ah, Miss Leslie! we are but strangers, newly met, within this hour; but we Creoles are the children of a southern clime, and our passions are gigantic as the palms which wave above your head – rapid in growth as the lilies on the breast of yonder lake. Love, with us, is a flame; suppressed, it is true, yet needing but one spark from the torch of beauty to cause a conflagration."

"Sir!" cried Cora, indignantly.

The young girl felt that the Creole's burning, passionate words veiled a meaning which was an insult to her.

"Nay, hear me, hear me, Cora," continued Augustus Horton; "there is, perhaps, a secret; there is, it may be, a fatality which overshadows your young life. Be mine, and none shall ever taunt you with that fatal secret; be mine, and you shall be the proudest beauty in Louisiana, the queen of New Orleans, the idol of your lover's devoted heart; be mine, and the debt owed me by your father shall be cancelled; be mine, and I will tear into a hundred fragments the bill which I hold for fifty thousand dollars, and which it will half ruin Gerald Leslie to pay."

Her eyes flashing, her bosom heaving with offended modesty, Cora Leslie rose from her chair.

"Toby," she called, without even replying by so much as a look to the planter's appeal.

"Cora Leslie, what would you do?" exclaimed the Creole, rising.

"Toby!" repeated Cora.

"Beware, young lady!"

The mulatto appeared in answer to the summons of his young mistress.

"Toby, you will conduct this gentleman to the gates of my father's grounds, and remember that if he ever again dares to present himself here, it will be your duty to refuse him admittance. You hear?"

"Yes, mistress."

"Go, sir," said Cora, looking at Augustus for the first time since she had risen from her seat; "I am but a stranger in New Orleans, and you have done much to enlighten me as to the character of its inhabitants. You have done well to choose the hour of a father's absence to insult his only daughter. Go!"

"I obey you, Miss Leslie," answered Augustus, white with rage, and trembling in every limb with suppressed passion. "Believe me, I shall not forget our interview of to-day, and shall take an opportunity to remind you of it on some future occasion. For the present I am your debtor; but trust me, the hour of settlement will come between us, when you shall pay dearly for this insolence. In the meantime," he added, turning to the mulatto, "in order to teach your young mistress her proper position, be good enough to relate to her the story of Francilia."

With one savage glance at the indignant girl, he hurried down the terrace steps, sprang into the saddle, put spurs to his horse, and rode off at a furious gallop.

"Francilia," exclaimed Cora; "Francilia! what could he mean? Speak, Toby, tell me, who was this Francilia?"

The mulatto hung his head, and was silent.

"Speak, I say," repeated Cora.

"Francilia – was – a slave, belonging to Mr. Leslie, Miss Cora."

"Well, then, what could she have in common with me? Why did that man cast her name in my face as an insult?"

Toby made no reply.

"You do not answer me. Good Heavens! a terrible light flashes upon me. Speak, speak!" cried the excited girl, grasping the arm of the slave in her slender hand, "Toby, speak!"

The mulatto fell on his knees at the feet of his young mistress, and cried imploringly:

"Miss Cora, in the name of mercy, do not look at me thus.

"Toby, tell me," murmured Cora, in a voice hoarse with emotion; "who was my mother?"

"Mistress, dear mistress, for pity's sake do not ask me. I have promised not to reveal—"

"You said just now that you loved me," answered Cora; "if you spoke the truth, prove your affection; tell me who was my mother?"

"Your mother—" faltered the slave; "no, no, I cannot, I dare not."

"But I command you – nay, I implore."

"Your mother – was called – Francilia."

"Oh, merciful Heaven, have pity upon me!" cried Cora, hiding her face in her hands: then, after a long pause, she said sorrowfully–

"And I did not even know the name of my mother. Francilia! a slave! this then is the secret of my life. Alas! she is dead: is she not?"

"She is."

"Dead, far from her child, who was not even permitted to weep for her."

"Thank Heaven that you do not curse her memory," murmured Toby, rising.

"Curse her!" exclaimed Cora; "would that I could embrace her, as I do you," she added, throwing her arms about the old man's neck.

"Me, Miss Cora! me, a mulatto!" remonstrated Toby, gently repulsing her.

"What of that? Does not the same blood flow in our veins? are we not of the same down-trodden race? Ah, speak, speak, Toby, you knew my mother; tell me of her; you see I am calm, I can listen."

She drew the mulatto to one of the garden-chairs, and, forcing him to sit down, placed herself at his feet; her hand in his; her dark eyes raised to his face.

"Francilia was but fifteen years of age," Toby began, "when a slave merchant brought her to Mr. Leslie; she was a Quadroon, beautiful as you are, though her skin was not so white. She had long black hair, and large dark eyes, whose sweet and gentle glance I can see again in yours. She was at first employed in the service of Mrs. Leslie. Oh, Heaven! poor child, how happy and light-hearted she was then; her joyous voice warbling the soft melodies of her nation; her merry laugh ringing through the corridors of the house. I saw her, and I dared to love her! That time was the happiest of my life, for she too loved me. Fools that we were. What right has the slave to love? The slave who belongs to another. One day, Francilia left for Saint Louis, with her master and mistress. They were to be absent some weeks. I was to remain behind. In bidding me farewell she left me this silver ring, which I wear on my finger. I would give it you, dear mistress, but I have sworn to keep it till my death. When Francilia – returned – she—"

The slave paused, overcome by emotion.

"Speak, speak, Toby!" said Cora.

"Oh, for pity's sake, do not accuse her! You know not what it is to be a slave, bound to obey, body and soul, the commands of a master. Is not even resistance a crime? When Francilia returned she had become your father's mistress. She confessed all to me, with tears, and heart-rending grief! A terrible rage possessed me! I was like a drunken man! If, in that moment, Mr. Leslie had appeared before me, I know that I should have become a murderer. But the habit of suffering teaches resignation to the slave. This first fury past, I felt my energy abandon me, and I could only weep with Francilia over our vanished happiness. Alas, poor child, she no longer laughed, she no longer sang!"

"Poor girl! poor girl!"

"It was only when you came into the world," continued Toby, "that she seemed to re-attach herself to life, and I, bestowing on you all the deep devotion that I had felt for her – forgive me, Miss Cora, I loved you as if you had been my own child."

"Dear Toby."

"But she – oh, how she loved you. With more than a mother's love; with the love of the slave, who knows that even her child is not her own, but is a slave like herself – and who dares not slumber beside the cradle of her infant, for they take away the children while the mother sleeps, and she awakes, perhaps, to find the cradle empty."

"Oh, cruel, cruel!"

"But this was not the fate with which you were threatened. Mr. Leslie had married a vain and capricious woman. They had no children, and his life was not a happy one. His love for you was intense – all the more intense, as he was compelled to conceal from all an affection which would have been considered a weakness. Your father's love for you had reassured Francilia, when one day (you were then four years old), he announced his determination of taking you to England. Francilia did not utter a word; the silent tears filled her mournful eyes. But when they tore you from her arms, she burst into a tempest of sobs, and fell insensible to the ground."

"Yes, yes, I remember."

"But all that is nothing!" cried the slave, his eyes flashing with vengeful fury; "nothing to—. Yet, no, no! I have no more to tell."

"But I insist on knowing all," exclaimed Cora, vehemently. "What became of my unhappy mother? How did she die?"

"On his return from Europe, Mr. Leslie found her tranquil, and apparently resigned; but the glance of those mournful black eyes became an eternal reproach, which irritated and tormented him. He sent her to work on the plantation; but for some reason or other, go where he would, he was always meeting her, always encountering the same melancholy look, which seemed to ask him for her child. At last he could endure it no longer. He sold her."

"Oh, Heaven!" exclaimed Cora.

"He sold her to a man of the name of Craig – a bad man – who, under the mask of a sanctimonious life, concealed the base heart of a profligate and a villain. He thought, on purchasing the slave, that he would succeed her late master in her good graces; but finding that he could obtain nothing by persuasion, he would have had recourse to violence, when Francilia seized a knife and buried its blade in her heart."

"Oh, my mother, my murdered mother!"

"A negro belonging to this Craig stole the knife, which he gave to me. I have it still."

Cora sank on her knees, the tears streaming from her eyes, her clasped hands uplifted to Heaven.

"Alas, beloved mother!" she cried, "martyr to the base and cruel laws of this accursed land, it is after fifteen years that your daughter learns your unhappy fate; after fifteen years that she weeps for your memory!"

CHAPTER IX.
THE DAUGHTER'S ACCUSATION.

CORA SHIELDS THE MULATTO FROM THE RAGE OF GERALD LESLIE

Neither Cora nor Toby were aware that there had been a listener during the latter part of their conversation; but it was not the less a fact. Gerald Leslie had returned unobserved by either of the excited speakers, and, arrested by the passionate gestures of the mulatto slave, had lingered in the background, anxious to discover the cause of his agitation.

His anger was terrible when he found that the fatal secret, which it had been the business of his life to conceal from Cora, was now revealed. But he still lingered, anxious to hear all.

"Toby," murmured Cora, rising from her knees; "tell me, where did they bury my mother?"

"Her grave is half-hidden in the thickest depths of a wood of magnolias upon the borders of Silas Craig's plantation. I carved a rustic cross and placed it at the head."

"You will conduct me to the spot, Toby?" asked Cora.

At this moment Gerald Leslie rushed forward, and, springing towards Toby, lifted his riding-whip as if about to strike the mulatto, when Cora flung herself between them.

"Strike me rather than him!" she exclaimed; then turning to the slave, she said quietly, "Go, Toby! I swear to you that while I live none shall harm so much as a hair of your head."

The mulatto lingered for a moment, looking imploringly at Gerald Leslie.

"Forgive me, Master, if I have spoken," he murmured, pleadingly.

"I will not have you excuse yourself," said Cora; "you have only done your duty. Go!"

Toby bent his head and slowly retired. Cora stood motionless, with her arms folded, her eyes fixed upon Gerald Leslie.

"Well," she said, "why do you not strike me? Who am I that your hand has not already chastised my insolence? Your daughter? No! The child of Francilia, a quadroon, a slave! Prove to me, sir, that I am before my master; for if I am indeed your daughter, I demand of you an account of your conduct to my mother."

"You accuse me! You, Cora!" exclaimed Gerald Leslie.

"I am ungrateful, am I not? Yes, another father would have allowed this child to grow up to slavery; while you, ashamed of your paternal love, as if it had been a crime, you tore me from my mother's arms, in order that I might forget her; in order to withdraw me from the curse which rested upon me; to efface, if possible, the last trace of this fatal stain!"

"What could I have done more than this, Cora?"

"You could have refrained from giving me life! You sent me to England; you caused me to be educated like a princess. Do you know what they taught me in that free country? They taught me that the honour of every man, the love of every mother, are alike sacred."

"It is, then, with my affection that you would reproach me!" replied Gerald Leslie, mournfully. "I would have saved you, and you accuse me, as if that wish had been a crime! I snatched you from the abyss that yawned before your infant feet, and in return you curse me! Oh, remember, Cora, remember the cares which I lavished upon you! Remember my patient submission to your childish caprices; the happiness I felt in all your baby joys; my pride when your little arms were twined about my neck, and your rosy lips responded to my kisses?"

"No, no!" exclaimed Cora; "do not remind me of these things. I would not remember them, for every embrace I bestowed upon you was a theft from my unhappy mother."

"Your mother! Hold, girl! do not speak to me of her! for though I feel that she was innocent of the hazard of her birth, I could almost hate her for having transmitted to you one drop of the accursed blood which flowed in her veins."

"Your hatred was satisfied," replied Cora, bitterly. "You sold her! The purchase-money which you received for her perhaps served to pay for the costly dresses which you bestowed upon me! The diamonds which have glittered upon my neck and arms were perhaps bought with the price of my mother's blood!"

"Have a care, Cora! Beware how you goad me to desperation. I have tried to forget – nay, I have forgotten that that blood was your own! Do not force me to remember!"

"And what if I do remind you! what would you do with me?" asked Cora. "Would you send me to your plantation to labour beneath the burning sun, and die before my time, worn out with superhuman toil? No! sell me rather. You may thus repair your ruined fortunes. Are you aware that one of your creditors, Augustus Horton, offered, only an hour ago, the fifty thousand dollars that you owe him as the price of your daughter's honour?"

"Oh, Heaven!" exclaimed Gerald Leslie; "all this is too terrible!" then flinging himself upon his knees at Cora's feet, he clasped her hands passionately in his own. "Cora, Cora, have pity upon me! What would you ask of me? What would you have me do? My crime is the crime of all. Is the punishment to fall upon me alone? Am I alone to suffer? I, who have sacrificed my honour – yes, Cora, my honour as a colonist – to the claim of paternal love? Do you know that every citizen in New Orleans would blame and ridicule me for my devotion to you? Do you know that I am even amenable to the laws of Louisiana for having dared to educate your mind and enlighten your understanding? See, I am on my knees at your feet. I, your father, humiliate myself to the very dust! Do not accuse me; in mercy, do not accuse me!"

Cora's beautiful face was pale as ashes, her large dark eyes distended, but tearless.

"Upon my knees, beside my mother's grave," she said, solemnly, "I will ask her spirit if I can forgive you."

She released herself from her father's grasp, and hurried into the house before he could arrest her. The planter rose from the ground and looked mournfully after his daughter, but he did not attempt to follow her.

* * * * * * * *

Later in the evening Gerald Leslie returned to New Orleans, and spent the long hours of the night alone in his solitary office face to face with ruin and despair.

The one crime of his youth had risen to torture his remorseful soul – ghastly and horrible shadow, it pursued the sinner in every place; it appeared at every moment. Repentance only could lay the phantom at rest, and he was now only learning to repent.

He had never before looked upon his conduct to the beautiful quadroon, Francilia, in the light of a crime. What had he done which was not done every day by others? What was she, lovely and innocent being as she was, but a slave – his property – bought with his sordid gold – his to destroy as he pleased?

Her melancholy death he looked upon as an unhappy accident, for which he himself was in no way responsible. That crime rested upon Silas Craig's overburdened soul.

Gerald Leslie utterly forgot that had he not been heartless enough to sell the mother of his only child, this cruel fate would never have been hers.

But now the consequences of his crime had overtaken him in a manner he had never dreamed of; Cora, his beloved, his idolized child, accused and cursed him as the murderer of her mother.

It was too horrible.

He dared not remain at the summer pavilion. He dared not meet the reproachful glances of those eyes which appeared to him as the ghostly orbs of the late Francilia. No, alone in his office, surrounded only by the evidences of commerce, and the intricate calculations of trade, he endeavoured to forget that he had a daughter, and a daughter who no longer loved him.

* * * * * * * *

And where all this time was Cora? With the Venetian shutters of her apartment closed; with the light of day excluded from her luxurious apartment, she lay with her head buried in the satin cushions of her couch, weeping for the mother whose mournful face she could scarcely recall – weeping for the father whose youthful sins she had so lately learned.

Bitter, bitter were the thoughts of the young girl, whose life had heretofore been one long summer's sunshine.

She, the courted, the caressed, the admired beauty of a London season – she was a slave – an Octoroon – a few drops only of the accursed blood of the African race were enough to taint her nature and change the whole current of her life.

Her father loved her, but he dared only love her in secret. The proud colonists would have laughed aloud at the planter's affection for his half-caste daughter. And he, too, Gilbert Margrave, the poet painter; he, whose every glance and every word had breathed of admiration, almost touching upon the borders of love; would doubtless ere long know all; and he, too, oh, bitter misery, would despise and loathe her!

Oh, thank Heaven, the unhappy girl wronged the noble nature of the English heart! She knew not that to the Briton there is no such word as slavery. She knew not that in a free country the lowest labourer in the fields has as full a right to law and justice as the proudest noble in the land.

CHAPTER X.
THE YOUNG LOVERS.

Camillia and Paul Lisimon were no longer children. The young heiress had attained her nineteenth year, while Don Juan's protégé was, as our readers are aware, two years her senior.

Paul still lived at the Villa Moraquitos. He occupied a small but neatly-furnished apartment, upon the upper floor. Here were arranged the books he loved; here he often sat absorbed in study till the early morning hours sounded from the clocks of New Orleans, and the pale stars faded in the purple river.

Deep in the quiet night, when all the household were sleeping; when the faintest footfall awoke a ghostly echo in the awful stillness of the house, the young student, forgetful of the swiftly-passing hours, toiled on, a steady traveller on the stony road which leads to greatness.

It was to Silas Craig, the attorney, that Don Juan Moraquitos had articled his protégé, much to the dislike of the young man, who had a peculiar aversion to the usurer.

"Let me be with any other lawyer in New Orleans rather than with that man," he said; "I can never tell you how deep a contempt I have for his character."

Don Juan laughed aloud.

"His character! my dear Paul," he replied, "what in mercy's name have you to do with the man's character? Silas Craig is a hypocrite! a profligate, who covers his worst vices with the all-sheltering cloak of religion. Granted! He is not the less one of the cleverest lawyers in New Orleans, and the fittest person to be entrusted with the cultivation of your splendid intellect."

These conversations were perpetually recurring between Don Juan and his protégé, prior to the signing of the articles which were to bind Paul Lisimon to the detested attorney; and the young man, finding that all his remonstrances were in vain, and fearing that if he objected too strongly to being articled to Silas Craig the business would terminate in his being compelled to lead a life of hopeless idleness, made no further difficulty about the matter; and some weeks after the signing of the articles, he took his seat in the office of Mr. Craig.

It was not long before Paul Lisimon discovered that there was a decided disinclination on the part of the attorney to initiate him even in the merest rudiments of his profession. He might have sat in the office reading the paper and lolling in a rocking-chair all day if he had pleased, but whenever he sought for employment he was put off with some excuse or other, more or less plausible.

An idle young man would have been delighted with this easy life, – not so Paul Lisimon. Kind and liberal as Don Juan Moraquitos had been to him, the proud spirit of the young man revolted against a life of dependence. He yearned not only to achieve a future career, but to repay the obligations of the past – to erase the stain of dependence from his youth; to pay for the education which had been given him by favour. Thus, where another would have rejoiced in the idleness of Silas Craig's office; where another would have abandoned himself to the dissipated pleasures that abound in such a city as New Orleans; where another would have snatched the tempting chalice which youthful passion offered to his lips, Paul Lisimon, in very defiance of his employer, slowly but surely advanced in the knowledge of the profession whose ranks he was predestined to join.

Strange to say, Don Juan, instead of praising and encouraging the industry of his protégé, laughed and ridiculed him for his determined labours.

"You are the most extraordinary young man I ever met with, Paul," said the Spaniard. "Where others of your age would be haunting the gaming-house, which, in spite of our laws for their suppression, secretly exist in New Orleans – where others would be nightly visitants of the theatre and the cafe, you are forever brooding over those stupid books."

"Other men are perhaps born to fortune," answered Paul, with quiet dignity; "remember, dear sir, I have to achieve it."

"Nay, Paul; how do you know what intentions a certain elderly Spanish gentleman may have with regard to a document called a will?"

"Heaven forbid, sir," replied Paul, "that I should ever seek to fathom those intentions; and if you allude to yourself, permit me to take this opportunity of declaring that I would not accept one dollar, even were your misguided generosity to seek to bequeath it to me."

"Santa Maria, Mr. Lisimon, and why not, pray?" asked Don Juan, laughing at the young man's impetuosity.

"Because I would not rob her who has the sole claim upon your fortune."

"My little Camillia; she will be rich enough in all conscience. Ah, Paul," added the Spaniard, looking somewhat searchingly at Lisimon, "it is a serious matter for a father to have such a daughter as Camillia Moraquitos to dispose of; a beauty and an heiress! Where in all New Orleans shall I find the man rich enough or noble enough to be her husband?"

Paul Lisimon winced as if he had received a thrust from a dagger.

"You will consult your daughter's heart, sir, I trust," he murmured hesitatingly; "even before the claims of wealth?"

The old Spaniard's brow darkened, and his sombre black eyes fixed themselves upon Paul's face with a sinister and penetrating gaze that boded little good to the young man. No more was said upon the subject between the two men. Paul did not relax his industry by one iota after this conversation. The enervating pleasures of the rich could not win him from the stern routine of toil and study.

Perhaps the reader has already guessed the fatal truth.

Paul Lisimon, the unknown dependent upon a rich man's bounty, the penniless lad who knew not even the names of his parents, or of the country which had given him birth – Paul loved the peerless daughter of the wealthy Don Juan Moraquitos; and was it to be wondered that he loved her?

From her childhood he had seen her daily, and had seen her every day more beautiful – more accomplished.

She possessed, it is true, much of the pride of her father's haughty race; but that pride was tempered by the sweetness of Olympia Crivelli; and it was a high and generous sentiment that led the young girl to hate a meanness or falsehood with even a deeper loathing than she would have felt for a crime.

But to Paul Lisimon, Camillia was never proud. To him she was all gentleness; all confiding affection. The very knowledge of his dependence, which had been dinned into her ears by Don Juan, rendered her only the more anxious to evince a sister-like devotion which should take the sting from his position.

Instinctively she knew, that in spite of all outward seeming that position was galling to the proud boy. Instinctively she felt that nature in creating Paul Lisimon had never intended him to fill a subordinate position. He was one of those who are born for greatness, and who, constrained by the cruel trammels of circumstances, and unable to attain their proper level, perish in the flower of youth, withered by the blighting hand of despair.

So died the poet Chatterton, a victim to the suicide's rash madness. So dies many a neglected genius, whose name is never heard by posterity.

Paul loved the heiress; loved her from the first hour in which she had soothed his boyish anguish at the loss of his patron Don Tomaso; loved her in the tranquil years of their youthful studies; loved her with the deep devotion of manhood, when his matured passion burst forth in its full force, and the flickering light became an unquenchable and steady flame.

He did not love in vain.

No, as years passed on, and the fair bud changed to the lovely blossom, Camillia's feelings changed towards her father's protégé. No longer could she greet him with a sister's calm smile of welcome. The ardent gaze of his dark eyes brought the crimson blush to her cheek and brow; her slender hand trembled when it rested in his – trembled responsive to the thrill which shook the young man's strong frame; her voice faltered as she addressed him, and her Southern eyes veiled themselves beneath their sheltering lashes, and dared not uplift themselves to his.

She loved him!

Happy and cloudless sunshine of youth. They loved, and earth became transformed into a paradise – the sky a roof of sapphire glory; the sunny river a flood of melted diamonds. The magic wand of the young blind god, Cupid, changed all things round them into splendour.

They dreamed not of the future. They thought not of the stern policy of a father, implacable in the pride of wealth. No, the distant storm-cloud was hidden from their radiant eyes.

"My Camillia," exclaimed the young man; "think you I can fail to achieve greatness when your love is to be the crown of the struggle? Think you I can falter on the road that leads to success, when your eyes will be the lode-stars to guide my way?"

The reader will see, therefore, that love and ambition went hand in hand in the soul of Paul Lisimon, and that higher motives than the mere lust of gain, or even the hope of glory, beckoned him on to victory.

It is not to be expected that Camillia Moraquitos was without suitors amongst the higher classes of New Orleans.

Had she been blind, lame, hump-backed, red-haired, a vixen, or a fury, there would yet, doubtless, have been hundreds ready to kneel before the charm of her father's wealth, and to declare the heiress an angel. But when it is remembered that her future fortune was only exceeded by her glorious beauty, it will be thought little marvel that she had a host of admirers ever ready to flock round her at her father's soirees, to attend her in her drives, to haunt her box at the opera or the theatre, and to talk of her beauty in all the coffee-houses of New Orleans. Our readers must remember that there is much in this chief city of Louisiana, which resembles rather a French than an English town. The inhabitants are many of them of French extraction. The coffee-houses – or *cafés* as they are called – resemble those of Paris; the gambling houses and theatres are Parisian in arrangements, and the young men of the upper classes have much of the polish of our Gallic neighbours, mingled with not a little of their frivolity.

Amongst the many suitors for the hand of Camillia Moraquitos was no less a person than Augustus Horton.

But the young planter did not love the Spanish beauty; there was something terribly repellent in the haughty spirit of Camillia to those whom she did not love, and Augustus Horton's pride was wounded by the thought that his attentions could possibly be disagreeable to any woman whom he condescended to honour by a preference. It was not love, therefore, which made him so constant in his attendance on the young beauty. No; mercenary motives, mingled with the resolute obstinacy of wounded pride, determined him to win the heiress from all competitors. He would not confess, even to himself, that there was any fear of his failing to attain the prize. He despised the young fops who whispered soft speeches and high-flown compliments into the unheeding ear of the disdainful girl, and, thinking these his only rivals, dreamt not of defeat.

In all the planter's visits to the Villa Moraquitos he had never yet encountered Paul Lisimon.

The young Mexican scrupulously held himself aloof from the rich and frivolous guests who assembled in Don Juan's splendid mansion.

In vain did the Spaniard bid his protégé to join in the festivities at the villa. In vain did Camillia reproach her lover with coldness and neglect, Paul was inexorable.

"So, Camillia," he said, when the young girl remonstrated with him, "I should hear your father's guests ask each other in the superb disdain of their Creole insolence, 'Who is this Mr. Lisimon?' I wait the time, Camillia, when my own exertions shall have made this simple and now unknown name of Lisimon familiar to every citizen in New Orleans."

While the soft echoes of piano and guitar floated through the luxurious saloons; while the rich contralto voice of Camillia, mingling with the chords of her guitar, enchanted her obsequious listeners, Paul toiled in his lonely chamber, only looking up now and then from his books and papers, to listen for a few brief moments to the sounds of laughter and revelry below.

"Laugh on!" he exclaimed, as a sarcastic smile curved his finely-moulded lips; "laugh on, frivolous and ignorant ones – whisper unmeaning compliments, and murmur inanities to my peerless Camillia! I do not fear you; for it is not thus she will be won."

Augustus Horton was a rich man; he belonged to one of the best families in New Orleans, and the old Spaniard knew of no one better suited as a husband for his beloved daughter.

Don Juan therefore encouraged the young planter's addressess, though at the same time thoroughly resolved to throw him off, should any richer or more aristocratic suitor present himself.

Camillia knew nothing of her father's intentions. All her admirers were alike indifferent to her, for her heart was irrevocable given, and her faith irrevocably pledged, to Paul Lisimon.

While these changes had been slowly working amongst the heads of the household, the hand of Time had not been idle in the humbler chambers of the Villa Moraquitos.

White hairs were mingled in the black locks of the mulatto woman Pepita; the negress Zara was bent with age, and Tristan, the negro lad, had become a man – a man with powerful passions and a subtle and cunning nature, hidden beneath the mask of pretended ignorance and simplicity.

He could sing grotesque songs, and dance half-savage dances, as in the early days of his young mistress's youth, when he was Camillia's only playfellow. He knew a hundred tricks of jugglery, sleight of hand by which he could amuse an idle hour, and even now he was often admitted to display his accomplishments before the Spanish girl, her devoted attendant Pepita, and her old governess, Mademoiselle Pauline Corsi, who still remained with her, no longer as instructress, but in the character of companion and friend.

We have as yet refrained from speaking of the Frenchwoman; but as she may by and bye play by no means an insignificant part in the great life drama we are relating, it is time that the reader should know more of her.

Pauline Corsi was but seventeen years old when she first came to Villa Moraquitos as the preceptress of Camillia, then a child of six. She was therefore thirty years of age at the time of which we write.

But although arrived at this comparatively mature period of life, she still retained much of the girlish beauty of extreme youth.

Unlike most of her countrywomen, she was very fair, with large, limpid, blue eyes, and a wealth of showery flaxen curls. Small and slender, with delicate little feet and hands, there was much in her appearance to indicate patrician extraction. Yet she never alluded to her country or her friends.

She told Don Juan that she was an orphan, homeless, penniless, and friendless, glad to leave the shores of her sunny France for the chances of finding better fortune in the New World.

"And I have found better fortune," she would say, lifting her expressive eyes to the dark face of her haughty employer; "for where could I have hoped to meet a nobler patron, or to find dearer friends or a happier home, than I have here. Ah, bless you, noble Spaniard, for your goodness to the helpless stranger."

It was in the summer that Pauline Corsi first came to Villa Moraquitos, and it was in the winter of the same year that Don Tomaso Crivelli expired in the arms of his brother-in-law.

We must request the reader to bear this in mind, for on the accuracy of certain dates hangs much of the tale of mystery and crime which we are about to reveal.

The gossips of New Orleans were ready to insinuate that the Spaniard's heart would surely be in a little danger from the presence of so young and lovely a woman as the French governess, but they soon grew tired of whispering this, for it was speedily perceived by all who knew Don Juan Moraquitos that his heart was buried in the mausoleum of his fair young wife, Olympia, and that all the love of which his proud nature was capable of was lavished on his only child.

Some girls in the position of Pauline Corsi might have nourished ambitious hopes, and might have angled for the heart and hand of the wealthy Spaniard; but it was impossible to suspect the light-hearted and frivolous young Frenchwoman of the mean vices of the schemer. She was a thing of sunshine and gladness – gay and heedless as the birds she tended in her chamber, careless of the morrow as the flower that perfumed her balcony. So thought all who knew Pauline Corsi.

Did any of them know her rightly?

The hideous skeleton, Time, whose bony hand lifts, inch by inch and day by day, the dark and pall-like curtain that hangs before the vast stage of the future, can alone answer this question.

Camillia Moraquitos was much attached to her old governess. All her varied accomplishments she owed to Mademoiselle Corsi; and, far too generous and high-minded to consider the handsome salary paid to the Frenchwoman a sufficient recompense for her services, she looked upon Pauline's devotion to her as an obligation which could only be repaid by gratitude and affection.

The young heiress had often endeavoured to bestow some handsome present upon her instructress (a valuable article of jewelry – a ring, a chain, a bracelet), but always to be firmly, though kindly, repulsed.

"No Camillia," Mademoiselle Corsi would reply, "I will take no gift from you but affection – that is a priceless treasure. Bestow that upon me, and you would amply reward me for a lifetime of devotion: the brief years I have given to your instruction have been more than repaid by my pupil's love."

Haughty and reserved as Camillia was to mere acquaintances, she was almost foolishly confiding to those whom she loved.

She had never kept a secret from Pauline Corsi until within this last year, and even then she would have told all to her trusted companion, had she not been forbidden to do so by one whom she loved even better than the Frenchwoman.

This secret was the engagement between herself and Paul Lisimon.

"You will not breathe one word to a mortal of the vows which bind us till death, will you, my Camillia?" said the young man, as, intoxicated with happiness, he pressed his betrothed to his wildly throbbing heart.

"To no one, dearest," answered Camillia, "until your position will warrant you in asking my father's consent to our union. That is to say," she added hesitatingly, "to no one but Pauline. I shall be so anxious to talk of you, and I know I can trust her."

"Not one word to her, Camillia, as you love me," exclaimed Paul, with energy.

"What? you mistrust my faithful Pauline!"

"I mistrust no one," answered Lisimon; "yet, paradoxical as it may seem, I trust scarcely any one. To give your secrets into the keeping of another, is to give your life – nay, the better part of life; for those secrets appertain to the inmost sentiment of your heart. No, Camillia, tell nothing until that day comes, when, proud and triumphant, I can claim you before your father and the world."

"But you believe Pauline to be all that is good?" urged Camillia, her affectionate nature wounded by the warning of Paul.

"Yes, since you tell me so, dearest; but, young as I am in the winding ways of the world, I am older than you, and the experience of Silas Craig's office has taught me many iniquitous secrets."

Augustus Horton had, as our readers are aware, many business transactions with the attorney and usurer, Craig. Despising the man most completely, it yet suited the young planter's purpose to employ him, for Silas was a master in the evil arts of chicanery; a useful lawyer for all business, but above all useful in such affairs as were of too dark and secret a nature to bear exposure to the light of day.

He was the attorney employed by Augustus Horton, by Don Juan Moraquitos, and by most of the wealthiest men in the city of New Orleans; men who affected ignorance of his character, because his style of doing business suited their purpose.

It was at Silas Craig's office that Augustus Horton first saw Paul Lisimon.

The two men encountered each other in an office opening out of the private room occupied by the attorney.

Paul was seated at his desk copying a deed; he looked up only for a moment as the planter entered the apartment, and immediately returned to his work. He knew that the visitor was his rival, Augustus Horton, but, secure in the love of Camillia, he was utterly indifferent to his presence. Not so the planter. He looked long and earnestly at the handsome and Spanish face of the young Mexican.

Simply as Paul was dressed, in the loose linen coat and trousers suitable to the climate, with an open shirt collar of the finest cambric, under which was knotted a black silk handkerchief, there was something so distinguished in his appearance that Augustus Horton could not help wondering who this elegant stranger was who had found his way into Silas Craig's office. So great was his curiosity, that when his business with the lawyer was ended, he lingered to ask a few questions about the strange clerk.

"In goodness' name, Craig," he said, as he lit a cigar from a box of allumettes upon the attorney's desk, "who is that young aristocrat whom you have secured as a pigeon for plucking, under pretence of teaching him the law?"

"A young aristocrat!"

"Yes, a young man I saw in the next office. A Spaniard, I should imagine, from his appearance. Very dark, with black eyes and curling black hair."

Silas Craig laughed aloud.

"An aristocrat!" he exclaimed, "why, surely you must mean Paul Lisimon?"

"Who is Paul Lisimon?"

"Why, I thought you were a constant visitor at Villa Moraquitos!"

"I am so," replied Augustus.

"And you have never met Paul Lisimon?"

"Never, man! Don't question me, but answer me. Who is this Paul Lisimon?"

"My articled pupil, a young Mexican, a protégé of Don Juan's, who is studying for the law."

"Who is he, and where did he come from?" asked Augustus, eagerly.

"That no one knows," answered Craig; "the brother-in-law of Don Juan Moraquitos, Don Tomaso Crivelli, brought him to New Orleans thirteen years ago, when the little heiress was about six years old."

"Indeed!" muttered Augustus, biting his lip fiercely; "and the children were brought up together, I suppose?"

"They were."

"That explains all," said the planter, striding towards the door.

"All what?" asked Craig.

"No matter," replied Augustus Horton; and, without another word to the lawyer, he left the apartment and passed once more through the office where Paul Lisimon was seated.

This time it was with a glance of intense malignity that he regarded the young man, who, scarcely conscious of his presence, sat with his head bent over his work.

"So," exclaimed the planter, when he found himself alone; "I thought that you were an iceberg, Camillia Moraquitos, and that the burning breath of passion had never melted your frozen nature. I never dreamt that I had a rival; but the mystery is solved. This Mexican, this nameless dependent on your father's bounty, is doubtless he for whom you scorn the proudest suitors New Orleans can offer. I should have known that a woman is never utterly indifferent to a man's attentions save when she loves another. No matter, Camillia, you will find it no trifle to brave the hatred of Augustus Horton. My rival is younger and handsomer than I; it would be hopeless to attempt to win her love while he is by to sue and be preferred; but before the year is out, I will have thrust him from my pathway as I would an insolent slave on my plantation."

CHAPTER XI.
PAUL LISIMON'S RUIN IS PLOTTED BY HIS ENEMIES.

From the hour in which Augustus Horton first looked upon the noble face and form of Paul Lisimon, he entertained for the young Mexican that deadly and unrelenting hatred which jealousy alone can nourish.

Be it distinctly understood, the planter did not love Camillia Moraquitos.

Lovely as was the Spanish girl, there was one who, in the eyes of Augustus, was yet lovelier; and that one was Cora, the daughter of Gerald Leslie, and the hapless quadroon slave, Francilia.

Cora, the OCTOROON!

Yes, the fatal word which branded this lovely and innocent being is contained in those three syllables. She was an Octoroon, removed in the eighth degree from the African race, with a skin purely white as the tint of the lilies sleeping upon the lakes of her native Louisiana. *One drop* of the blood of a slave ran in her veins, poisoned her inmost life, and stamped her with the curse of Cain.

She was an OCTOROON!

Augustus Horton knew this. He knew, also, that Gerald Leslie was a ruined man; and he waited his time.

Cora had inspired in the proud heart of the planter one of those all-absorbing passions, which, in a bad man's heart, resemble the storm and tempest. They rage but to destroy. At any price, even at the price of his own soul as well as hers, she must be his.

The insult she had inflicted upon him in dismissing him from her presence had infuriated and humiliated him, but it had not abated one spark of the wild ardour of his guilty passion; notwithstanding this he was determined upon becoming the husband of Camillia Moraquitos.

The reader is already acquainted with the laxity of Louisianian morals. The wealthy Creole thought there could be no shame to the Octoroon in becoming his mistress. What was she but a creature of the inferior race, born to obey her master, the white man? With Camillia's fortune, added to his own ample wealth, Augustus Horton would have been one of the richest men in New Orleans. But the planter felt that he had discovered his real and only rival in the person of Paul Lisimon, the Mexican.

He was not slow to act upon this conviction. Early upon the morning after his first encounter with Paul, he entered the office in which the young man was seated, and asked to see Silas Craig.

Paul Lisimon raised his eyes, and recognized one of the most constant admirers of Camillia Moraquitos. But it was with a glance of supreme indifference that the Mexican regarded his rival. Augustus Horton felt the sting of that careless look; it was the glance of one who, secure in the affection of her he loves, is incapable of jealousy.

"Mr. Craig is within?" he enquired, addressing himself especially to Paul, though a coloured lad at a desk near was the person who answered all inquiries, and ushered the clients into Silas Craig's office.

"He is," answered Paul, quietly, dropping his eyes upon his work, and not lifting them as he spoke; "Marcus, take this gentleman's card to your master."

Silas was seated at his desk, a ledger open before him, and on the table by his side a large iron cash-box, the lid of which he dropped hurriedly as the young planter entered the office.

The ledger contained the secret accounts of the transactions of the mysterious gambling-house in Columbia Street. The cash-box was nearly filled with bank notes, lost in that den of iniquity by the miserable and deluded votaries of the gambler's green cloth-covered altar. Silas closed the ledger, which was secured with massive brass locks, the key of which the usurer wore hanging to a thick gold chain, which was never removed night or day – the iniquitous volume was further secured by being placed in an iron chest, proof against fire and thieves.

The money gained by these shameful transactions was sent monthly to New York, where it was banked in the name of Craig & Co., solicitors.

This was done to prevent the possibility of the losers of this money tracing it, by the numbers of the notes, into the hands of the usurer.

These precautions may seem superfluous, but they were no more than necessary. Silas Craig felt that he was carrying on an infamous traffic. He knew that were his name revealed as the proprietor of a house which bore no very high reputation for fair play, and in which several deeds of darkness were strongly suspected to have been committed, universal hatred and execration would be heaped upon his guilty head. More than this, there was a tribunal he dreaded more than all the established courts of New Orleans; he knew that for such an offence as his the infuriated citizens would have recourse to the horrors of Lynch Law.

He glanced round suspiciously as Augustus Horton entered the room, and thrust the locked ledger into an open drawer in his desk.

"My dear Augustus," he said, with his accustomed conciliatory smile, "this is indeed an agreeable surprise. I scarcely expected to see you so soon again."

"I dare say not," answered the planter, coolly, taking out a cigar and lighting it at the taper by which Craig sealed his letters.

"And may I ask to what I owe the honour of this visit?" said Silas, looking, with considerable curiosity, at his client's thoughtful countenance.

"I'll tell you, Silas Craig. That young Mexican yonder; that Limison, or Lismion, or whatever his name may be – that hanger-on and dependent of Juan Moraquitos, must leave your office."

Silas started and glanced wonderingly at the planter.

"Ay, you may stare," said Augustus; "never you mind my motives. I say he must go!"

"But, my dear young friend, my impetuous friend, that is utterly impossible. I have no particular affection for Mr. Paul Lisimon, I assure you, but his articles have been signed."

"Let them be cancelled, then; let the fellow be kicked out of the office."

Silas looked thoughtfully at his visitor, and then rubbing his hands, said, with a sly chuckle,

"But, my dear Mr. Horton, allow me to remind you that, in the first place, I have no excuse for cancelling these articles, or for kicking Paul Lisimon out of my office; and that, in the second, I cannot see why I am bound to comply with any absurd whim which even my most important client may happen to take into his head."

Augustus Horton threw his cigar aside with a contemptuous and impatient gesture.

"I am not used," he said, with chilling hauteur, "to ask for any service for which I am not prepared to pay liberally. Send this young man about his business – making it appear that he has been to blame in the affair, and besides what you lose by cancelling the articles I will give you five thousand dollars."

"Send him about his business?"

"Yes. If possible in such a manner as to disgust Don Juan with his protégé."

A strange smile illuminated Silas Craig's crafty countenance.

"Disgust Don Juan with his protégé?" he said.

"Yes, find this fellow out in some piece of low trickery or dishonour. He is not obliged to be really guilty, if he only appears so."

"In such a manner that Don Juan may cast him off?" asked Silas, with the same meaning smile.

"Yes, do that, and I will double your reward. Instead of five thousand dollars I will give you ten."

"It's rather a critical business."

"Yes, but a sort of business that I should think is scarcely new to you, my worthy Silas," said Augustus, with a sneer.

That contemptuous curve of the lip was not lost upon Silas Craig; but the usurer himself entertained a consummate disdain for these men who despised his character, but were yet content to make use of him in deeds to which they would have been themselves ashamed to own.

"I think it can be done," he said quietly, "and I have no objection to do it, upon one condition—"

"And that is—"

"That, over and above the ten thousand dollars I am to receive on the day on which Paul Lisimon is dismissed from this office and from the house of his patron, Don Juan, you give me twenty thousand more upon the day of your marriage with Camillia Moraquitos."

The planter bit his lip, and his brow grew crimson with vexation.

"How do you know that I have any thought of seeking to win Camillia Moraquitos for my wife?" he asked, angrily.

"How do I know?" answered the usurer. "Augustus Horton, it may please your proud nature to despise me, although you come here to demand my services. Despise my code of morality, if you will, but do not despise my powers of penetration. There is not a client who enters this office whose inmost thoughts I have not reckoned up before he has been five minutes in my company. It is a knack we lawyers acquire, if we are fit for our business. Shall I tell you your motive in wishing to thrust Paul Lisimon from my office?"

"Yes, if you can."

"You dread a rival in this handsome young man. You would brand his name, already an obscure one, with shame and infamy; you would cause him to be driven from the doors of Villa Moraquitos, and stamped with ignominy in the eyes of the woman who loves him."

"Yes," cried Augustus, fiercely; "I would do all this! Dog, what right has he to cross my path? I accede to your condition, Silas Craig, ten thousand down, and twenty thousand more upon my wedding day."

"Then the business shall be done."

"Soon?"

"Very soon."

"That is well: Silas, lose no time in turning the fellow from your doors, and let me be the first to hear of his dismissal. I shall not grudge you your reward."

As Augustus Horton left the office he once more flung a sinister glance at the articled clerk; but this time there was triumph as well as hatred in the flash of the planter's eyes.

As he glanced at Paul Lisimon the glitter of some gold ornaments hanging to the Mexican's watch chain caught his eye. Amongst these was an oval locket, of dead gold, ornamented with two initials in purple enamel.

The planter passed so close to Paul that he was enabled to distinguish these initials.

They were a C. and an M.

"So!" he muttered, as he mounted the thorough-bred Arabian waiting for him at the door of Silas Craig's house, "he wears a locket inscribed with her initials – a locket containing her portrait, no doubt. She loves him, then; but, by the blue sky above me, she shall be taught ere long to despise and loathe him."

Silas Craig was not long in putting his foul plot into execution.

In order to carry it out, he had recourse to a plan as subtle as it was diabolical.

The lawyer's private office communicated, as the reader is aware, with an outer apartment occupied by clerks.

There was but this one door of communication between the two rooms, and there was no other visible mode of entering the inner office.

But there was the secret entrance through the map of America, which communicated with the passage leading into the house in Columbia street. The existence of this secret passage was known only to Silas Craig, William Bowen, and the banker and manager of the gambling house.

It was by means of this very passage that the foul plot, which was to entrap Paul Lisimon, was to be carried out.

Three days after his interview with the planter, Silas Craig summoned the young Mexican to his private office.

"My dear Lisimon," he said, motioning Paul to a seat, "for once in my life I am tempted to desert business earlier than usual. I have an engagement to dine with my client, Mr. Horton. The dinner hour is five, and I have, unfortunately, an appointment here at half-past five with a wealthy old client of mine, who is going to bring me a few thousand dollars he wishes me to invest for him. Now, in this dilemma, I fancy, my dear Lisimon, that you can assist me."

Paul merely bowed. They were not alone in the office; one of the other clerks, a young man of the name of Morisson, was standing at the lawyer's desk waiting for further orders.

"What I want you to do, Lisimon, is to remain here till half-past five and receive the money from my client. You will give him an acknowledgement for the sum, and you will place the money, whether it should be in notes or gold, in this small cash-box, of which I will leave you the key. I shall also give you the key of the door of this office, which you will carefully lock on leaving the place. As there is no other communication, all will be perfectly secure. You understand?"

"Completely, Mr. Craig," said Paul.

"I thought you would be able to do this little bit of business for me," replied the lawyer, rising and locking his desk; "here are the keys," he added, handing Paul the key of the door and the smaller one belonging to the cash-box; "you will keep the office key in your possession until you see me to-morrow morning. Be very careful of it, for I have no duplicate. It's now half-past four, so I have not a minute to lose. You'll find my client, Mr. Graham, a curious countryfied old fellow, Lisimon, but I've no doubt you'll be able to manage him. Good afternoon!"

Silas left the office, followed by the clerk, Morisson; and Paul, taking up one of the New Orleans papers, prepared to await the expected visitor. The client arrived, punctual to his appointment, at half-past five. He was an elderly man, a planter, whose estate lay at a distance of several hundred miles from New Orleans, and who had the highest opinion of Silas Craig's professional and moral character.

"A worthy man," he would say, shaking his head wisely, when speaking of the money-lending lawyer; "a moral man, a church-going man, and a credit to New Orleans. I am sorry there are not more to follow his pious example."

Paul received the money, which was in the shape of a roll of dollar bills.

"I have the numbers of the bills in my pocket-book," said the old man, as he handed the packet to the Mexican; "I'm rather a cautious old fellow, you know, my dear sir."

Paul wrote an acknowledgement of the sum, and handed it to Silas Craig's client.

"Perfectly correct, perfectly correct, my dear Sir," Mr. Graham muttered, as he read it over– " 'Received of John Graham, fifteen thousand dollars,' – dated and signed. Thank you, Sir, and good evening."

Paul summoned the mulatto lad to show Mr. Graham out, and then, after locking the money in the cash-box – a small metal casket, which might have easily been carried in the ample pocket of Paul's loose linen coat – he left the office, and double-locked the door behind him.

"I think that's all right, Marcus," he said to the boy.

"Iss, massa."

"You sleep in this office, don't you?"

"Iss, massa."

"Then there's no likelihood of anyone entering that room without your being aware of it."

"No, massa; not unless Marcus was very deaf."

"Which, fortunately, you are not. Keep a sharp look out, my lad, and I'll give you half a dollar to-morrow."

Paul left the office and returned to Villa Moraquitos, where, for once in a way, he found Camillia alone with Mdlle. Corsi. Her father was absent at a dinner party, given by Augustus Horton.

This very dinner party was a portion of the villainous plot, concocted by Silas Craig and the planter, for the destruction of Paul Lisimon.

The evening flew by like some blessed dream to the young Mexican. Camillia was by his side; she sang to him wild and plaintive Spanish ballads, whose mournful and harmonious cadence drowned his soul in rapture. The words written in the love-breathing language of that Southern land, from whose orange groves and palaces the ancestors of Camillia had emigrated to Southern America.

A happy evening; alas! the very last of happiness that Paul was to taste for a long time to come.

But even in the society of Camillia Moraquitos, Paul could not quite repress a certain uneasiness about the money he had left in the cash-box in Silas Craig's office.

He disliked the responsibility of the trust which had been forced upon him by his employer, and was impatient to return the key of the office to its owner.

For this reason he was at his post earlier than usual the following morning.

Silas Craig did not enter the clerk's office till much later than his customary hour for beginning business. Morisson and one or two others began to speculate upon the probability of their employer having drank rather too freely at the planter's dinner table.

The attorney appeared in a peculiarly amiable temper that morning. He shook hands with Paul, spoke to each of the clerks, commended their work, and then, holding out his hand, said, very graciously, "Now, my dear Lisimon, the key of the office. I suppose Mr. Graham lodged that money in your hands last night?"

"He did, sir; you will find it in the cash-box."

Silas nodded and unlocked the door of the inner office. "Oh, by the bye," he said, "just step this way, Mr. Morisson; I have some directions to give you."

The clerk followed his employer into the office. Five minutes afterwards Morisson put his head out of the door: "Mr. Lisimon," he said, "you are wanted, if you please."

Paul hastened to the inner office. The lawyer was looking very grave, but he spoke in his usual friendly tone.

"Where did you say you put the money, my dear Lisimon?" he asked.

"In the small cash-box," replied Paul– "there!"

He pointed, as he spoke, to the table upon which he had left the cash-box on the preceding evening.

It was no longer there.

The young Mexican's olive cheek grew suddenly white.

This fact was observed by the clerk, who stood aghast looking on.

"You must be mistaken, Lisimon; you very likely placed the box in some other part of the office?"

"No!" cried Paul, with energy, "I left it on that table, and no where else. Come, Mr. Craig, this must be some jest of yours. You have removed the box since you entered the office, and are doing this to frighten me."

"Was there any box on yonder table when we entered this room, Morisson?" said Craig, addressing himself to the clerk.

"No, sir."

"You see, my dear Lisimon, it must be you who are jesting. Were you any other than the beloved protégé of my respected client, Don Juan Moraquitos, I should positively begin to be alarmed."

"Jesting!" exclaimed Paul; "I swear to you that before leaving this office last night, I locked the cash-box containing the dollar bills and placed it upon that table. Search where you will, Morisson," he said, looking at the clerk, who, at a whispered order from his employer, had begun to search the office, "unless there has been witchcraft about, you will find it there and nowhere else, for there I left it."

"Come, come, Mr. Lisimon," said Craig, in an altered tone, "this is really too absurd. We no longer believe in magic, or the juggleries of the fiend. You say you left the box in this apartment last night. It must therefore be here this morning – if you have spoken the truth."

"*If* I have spoken the truth!" echoed Paul, the hue of his cheeks changing from pale to crimson.

"Not a creature has entered this room since you left it," continued Silas; "for there is but one key to the door, and that has been in your possession until within the last ten minutes. The boy Marcus sleeps in the office; call him, Morisson."

The mulatto lad made his appearance.

"Marcus," said his master, "did any one enter this room last night?"

"No, massa, the door was locked."

"I know that; and no one entered by any means whatever?"

"No one, massa, unless de debil go through de keyhole."

"When Mr. Lisimon left this office last night, had he anything in his hand?"

"Nothing, massa."

"But he might have had something in his pocket," muttered Silas, in an under-tone.

Paul Lisimon turned upon his employer with indignant fury.

"Mr. Craig," he exclaimed, "could you dare to insinuate—?"

"No, Mr. Lisimon, it is rather too late in the day for insinuations," answered the attorney, with a sardonic laugh, "you were left in charge of a sum of money; you were told to place it in this room to which no one but yourself had access. The fact is only too clear; you have disgraced the bounty of your patron; you are a thief!"

"A thief!" shrieked Paul. The lawyer's gold-headed bamboo cane stood in one corner of the office; before the clerk, Morisson, could interpose, Paul Lisimon snatched this cane in his convulsed grasp, and bounding upon Silas Craig, struck him across the face.

"Liar!" he cried, "I see the drift of this double-dyed villainy. I am the victim of a plot, so demoniac, that I shudder at the blackness of its treachery. The money has been removed through *your* agency – removed in order that my name may be branded with a crime. I fear you not, vile schemer, be it yours to tremble, for Heaven looks down upon us, and will defend the innocent."

He rushed from the office, and had left the house before Silas recovered from the terror these words had struck to his guilty heart.

"Pursue him!" he cried, hoarse with fury; "pursue him, and drag him to prison. Yet, stay, it is too late now to overtake him. I know where to find him – at the Villa Moraquitos."

CHAPTER XII.
TRISTAN'S SECRET.

CAMILLIA RESCUED BY THE NEGRO

Tristan, the negro, sat in his little chamber, in that quarter of Don Juan's splendid mansion, which was devoted solely to the slaves.

A dark and gloomy shadow rested upon the inky brow of the negro. For some time past the watchful eye of his mother, the old negress, Zara, had detected her son's unhappiness, but she sought in vain to penetrate the cause. There was much of the savage in the character of this man, and even in his mother he sometimes inspired alarm and suspicion.

His was one of those natures, burning as Africa's skies, created, sometimes, like the venomous serpents of those tropical climes, only to terrify and to destroy.

But he was a privileged being in the house of Don Juan Moraquitos. He had saved the life of the Spaniard's idolized daughter.

Yes, only one brief year before the period of which we write, Tristan, the negro, had by his courage and activity preserved Camillia from a fearful death.

Late one evening the young girl and her governess had sat talking together in Camillia's luxurious boudoir. The slave Tristan had been admitted to the apartment to amuse the capricious beauty with his songs and antics. But Camillia had soon grown weary of this diversion, and turning to Mademoiselle Corsi, she said languidly,

"Tell Tristan to leave us, Pauline, he is noisy, and he wearies me."

Generous-hearted as was the Spanish girl, her education had taught her to look upon a slave as an inferior being, unblest with those finer feelings which demand our courtesy and consideration. She dismissed Tristan as she would have dismissed her lap-dog when tired of his antics. A black and gloomy frown obscured the negro's glittering eyes as he was thus unceremoniously ordered from the room.

It was unobserved by Camillia, but not unmarked by Pauline Corsi.

The slave retired, but he did not go far. Between the boudoir and the saloon there was an antechamber, the floor of which was covered with a square Persian carpet – a carpet of immense value, thick as velvet pile.

Upon this carpet, close to the door of the boudoir, Tristan threw himself, like a dog on the threshold of his master's apartment.

"She sends me from her," he said, bitterly; "I am noisy, and I weary her; it was not so in the days that are long gone by, when she and I were play-fellows."

The negro gone, Camillia reclined upon a sofa, and amused herself by looking over a pile of French novels, which had lately arrived from Paris. To do this she drew towards her a little inlaid table upon which stood an elegant reading lamp.

Pauline Corsi was seated at the other extremity of the apartment, working briskly at a large piece of embroidery, and lost in thought. She did not therefore observe the proceedings of her young pupil.

For some time Camillia read on undisturbed; but by-and-bye, growing weary of her book, she cast it from her with an impatient exclamation, and stretched out her hand to reach another from the volumes on the table beside her. In doing this she upset the reading lamp.

The glass globe broke with a crash; the inflammable oil and burning wick were spilled upon the gauzy muslin folds of her voluminous dress.

She uttered a shriek of horror, for in one brief moment she found herself in flames.

The negro heard that shriek; and, swift as the panther darting from his lair, he bounded from the threshold where he had been lying.

Losing all presence of mind, Camillia, followed by Pauline Corsi, rushed past the slave Tristan, and from the ante-chamber into the saloon beyond.

The flames, fanned by the current of air through which she passed, rose towards her head. In another moment she would have been lost.

But the preserver was at hand.

With a yell of agony, like that of a wild beast in its death-struggle with the hunter, the negro flung himself upon the floor of the ante-chamber, and tore up the heavy Persian carpet which covered the room; then, rushing upon Camillia, he enveloped her slender form in this massive fabric, and with his own hands extinguished the flames.

The Spaniard's daughter escaped unscathed from this terrible ordeal, but the hands of the slave were fearfully scorched and wounded.

Don Juan Moraquitos offered any reward he might choose to name to the deliverer of his child, but, to the Spaniard's astonishment, Tristan refused all his master's offers.

The Spaniard would have given him freedom, but the slave chose rather to stay in the house in which he had been born.

All gifts of money he also refused – refused with a gloomy determination which Don Juan and Camillia tried in vain to overcome.

"No!" he said, "let me stay with you, my master and my mistress. The poor slave, Tristan, asks no more."

In vain the old negress, Zara, pleaded with her son, imploring him to ask freedom for himself and his mother, that they might return to the native shore from which the captain of a slaver had brought them. He refused to listen to her entreaties, and turned from her with a gloomy scowl.

Don Juan and his daughter praised the fidelity of the slave, and promised him every privilege that could render his service a happy one. Only one person in that household divined the secret clue to the negro's strange conduct. That person was the seemingly frivolous and light-hearted Frenchwoman, Pauline Corsi.

A depth of penetration lurked beneath that girlish exterior. She read the true meaning of Tristan's conduct.

The slave – the negro – the thick-lipped and woolly-haired African – the lowest type of a despised and abhorred race, loved his mistress, the wealthy Spanish heiress, the beautiful and haughty Camillia Moraquitos!

CHAPTER XIII.
PAULINE CORSI OFFERS TO REVEAL A SECRET.

Silas Craig was right in his conjecture. Paul Lisimon went straight from the lawyer's office to the Villa Moraquitos.

It was there, and in the eyes of her he so dearly loved, and of the haughty benefactor of his youth, that the young Mexican was eager to disprove the lying accusation brought against him.

A THIEF!

His proud spirit revolted at the very thought of the base nature of the crime of which he was accused. Theft – the most contemptible, petty theft – a theft upon the employer who had trusted him!

He found Camillia within doors, and, in the presence of Pauline Corsi, told her the story of his wrongs.

The lovely eyes of the Spanish girl flashed with indignant fire.

"We always hated this man, Craig, by instinct, Paul," she said; "that instinct did not deceive us."

Pauline Corsi appeared to sympathize sincerely with the lovers, and expressed the utmost contempt for Silas Craig.

While Paul was seated by Camillia, her hand clasped in his, her large black eyes bathed in tears, yet lifted confidingly to his face, the sound of the footsteps of several men was heard upon the staircase without, and Don Juan Moraquitos entered the apartment, followed by Silas Craig.

The brow of the Spaniard was dark with passion, but beneath the red eyebrows of the lawyer, there sparkled the light of malice and cunning.

"Release the hand of that man, Camillia Moraquitos!" exclaimed Don Juan, with suppressed fury, as he beheld his daughter and Paul Lisimon seated side by side; "release his hand, or never again dare to call me father!"

The young girl raised her eyes to the face of the Spaniard, and met his angry gaze with a glance of calm defiance.

"Why should I take my hand from his?" she said, calmly; "we have been playfellows, companions, and friends from childhood. You have seen our hands locked together often ere to-day; why do you wish to part us now?"

Though the voice of the Spanish girl was calm and unfaltering, and although she met her father's gaze without one quiver of her snowy eyelids, her slender form trembled with emotion as she spoke.

"Shall I tell you why, Camillia?" asked her father.

"Yes; I wait to learn."

"Because Paul Lisimon, the man whose boyhood has been spent beneath this roof, whose education has been shared with you, who has ever been treated as a son, rather than as a dependent, that man is a thief!"

Had Camillia been unprepared for this accusation, the blow might, for a moment, have paralysed her. But she had heard all from Paul's own lips, and she was prepared for the worst.

"He is no thief!" she exclaimed, proudly; "were he that, he would not have come hither to seek for sympathy from Camillia Moraquitos."

"Deluded girl, he has been discovered in an act of daring robbery – robbery which is most contemptible, being allied to treachery of the basest nature. He was trusted, and he betrayed his trust."

The lip of the Spanish girl curled with unutterable scorn.

"Trusted!" she exclaimed, "trusted, did you say! Father, I ask you, by all your knowledge of mankind, by your faith in Nature's surest index, the human countenance, is *that* the man to trust any living creature?"

She pointed to Silas Craig as she spoke, and the lawyer quailed beneath her flashing glance. For a moment he shrunk back abashed and powerless to reply to the Spanish girl's disdainful words, then recovering himself with an effort, he said, with an assumed air of meekness,

"Donna Camillia is pleased to be severe. We lawyers are certainly not over trusting in our fellow men – we are too often deceived; but I thought I might safely trust the protégé of Don Juan Moraquitos. I did not think to find him a thief."

"Liar!" cried Paul Lisimon. "Dastard! *You* know that I am no thief. *You* know the base plot which has been planned by you – from what motive I know not – for my destruction. Now that all is past, I can see the base scheme from the very first. Your pretended confidence; your desire that I should remain alone in your office to receive a sum of money which you might have as well received yourself; your trusting me with the key – of which, *you say*, you have no duplicate; your simulated friendship, and your affected surprise this morning upon missing the casket containing the money; all these are so many links in the chain of infamy which you have woven around me; but through all I defy you. The money was taken from your office by no common robber; it was removed either by you, or by an agent in your employ."

"The inner office has but one door," answered Silas Craig, "you possessed the only key of that door – nay, more, the mulatto boy, Marcus, slept in the clerk's office, and must have heard anybody who attempted to enter the inner chamber. Heaven knows," ejaculated Silas, sanctimoniously, "how much grief I feel at the discovery of such baseness in the adopted son of my most respected client; but guilt such as yours must not, for the benefit of society, go unpunished."

Paul Lisimon turned from him with a gesture of loathing, and addressed himself to Don Juan.

"You hear this man," he said, "you hear him, yet you do not surely believe one word he utters. Look in his face, on which 'liar' is branded, in unmistakable characters, by the hand of Heaven; and then believe him if you can. My patron, my benefactor, friend and protector of my otherwise friendless youth; has any one action of my life, since I have shared the shelter of your roof, and eaten your bread – has any one action of my life given you reason to believe me the base and guilty wretch this man would have you think me? Speak, I implore you."

The young Mexican waited with clasped hands for Don Juan's reply. The Spaniard coldly averted his face. It seemed as if he, too, shrank from meeting that noble countenance.

"Circumstances speak too plainly, Mr. Lisimon," he said; "facts are incontrovertible – they are stronger than words, and they force me to believe."

"They force you to believe that the man, who has been reared beneath your own protection, has been guilty of an act worthy of one of the swell-mobsmen, or experienced burglars of New Orleans. One word more, Don Juan Moraquitos – it is the last with which I shall trouble you."

"I listen," replied the Spaniard.

"I appeal to you by the memory of the dead – by the memory of him who was more than a father to me – by the memory of the last hour of Don Tomaso Crivelli."

It seemed as if the sound of this name struck upon the most sensitive chord in the nature of the haughty Spaniard. He started as if he had been shot, and, dropping into a chair that stood near him, buried his face in his hands. Silas Craig lifted his eyes with a glance of pious horror.

"This is horrible!" he exclaimed; "the guilty wretch dares to call upon the name of the dead, dares to wound his noble benefactor's sensitive heart. Why delay any longer to reason with this hypocrite? The officers of justice are without, let them at once do their duty."

Silas Craig opened the door of the apartment as he spoke, and beckoned to three men who were waiting on the staircase.

"The police!" exclaimed Paul.

"Yes; they have a warrant for your arrest," replied Silas Craig. "You have carried it with a very high hand, Mr. Paul Lisimon, but you will sleep in jail to-night."

The young Mexican did not condescend to answer this speech, but, turning to Don Juan, he said with quiet dignity–

"Since this man's accusation appears to you stronger than my declaration of innocence, I cannot blame you, Sir, in believing him. I freely own that the chain of evidence forged against me is a damning one, but, sooner or later, the day will come when I will shatter that chain, link by link, and prove yonder wretch the basest of his kind. In the mean time, I would but ask one favour of you. I have papers and letters in my room, which are of priceless value to me, suffer me to gather those together before they convey me to prison."

Don Juan had not once lifted his head since the mention of his brother-in-law's name. He replied to Paul's request, in a broken voice,–

"Let him take the papers he speaks of," he answered, "I will be responsible for him."

The principal police-officer bowed. "I will accompany you to your rooms, Mr. Lisimon," he said, "and remain with you while you collect those papers."

"Father, father!" exclaimed Camillia; "can you suffer this – can you allow the companion of my youth to be sent to gaol as a common felon?"

"He merits no other fate," replied Don Juan; "he has proved himself unworthy of the name of an honest man."

"He has not done so," cried Camillia; "he is innocent!"

"What leads you to believe in his innocence?"

"My own instinct," replied the fearless girl.

Again the brow of Don Juan grew dark with fury.

"Your own instinct!" he exclaimed; "beware, girl, do not force me to believe you have another reason for thus defending this man. Do not compel me to despise you!"

While this conversation was passing between father and daughter, Paul Lisimon and the officer proceeded to the Mexican's apartment, which was situated, as the reader is aware, upon the upper floor of Villa Moraquitos; but the Spaniard's elegant abode was only elevated one story above the ground floor, so that the room occupied by Paul was not in reality more than eighteen feet above the garden, into which it looked. The police-officer followed his prisoner into the room, and seated himself near the door, while Paul unlocked his desk and examined its contents.

The papers which he wished to secure were a few brief notes that had been written to him, at different periods, by Camillia Moraquitos. The young girl had often slipped a few lines of affectionate encouragement into her lover's hand, at a time when the lynx eyes of strangers prevented their exchanging one tender word.

Paul Lisimon knew that brief as these letters were, they contained quite enough to betray the secret of the lovers, and to draw down upon Camillia all the terrors of a father's wrath.

He secured the little packet with a ribbon, which the Spanish girl had once worn in her hair, and thrusting the packet into his bosom, prepared to accompany the officer.

As they were about leaving the apartments, a low rap sounded upon the panel of the door.

The person who thus demanded admittance was the French governess, Pauline Corsi.

"Let me speak to your prisoner – alone – if only for a few moments?" she said, pleadingly, and with all the fascination peculiar to her manner; "let me speak to him, Monsieur, I implore!"

"You are welcome to speak to him, Mademoiselle," replied the officer, "but I regret to tell you that whatever you have to say, must be said in my presence."

The Frenchwoman shrugged her shoulders with a graceful gesture of vexation.

"That is very hard, Monsieur," she said, looking thoughtful.

"Nay, Mademoiselle Corsi," interposed Paul, who could not understand the Frenchwoman's desire to see him alone, "you can have nothing to say which this man may not hear. Speak freely; I have no secrets."

"But perhaps I have," answered Pauline. "See, Monsieur," she added, extending her plump little hand, upon one finger of which there sparkled a superb diamond ring, "tell me what you think of those diamonds."

Paul Lisimon started, for he recognized the ring. It was one he had often seen Camillia wear.

The French governess had been sent to him, then, by the devoted girl?

"They are magnificent stones, are they not, Monsieur?" repeated Pauline, still addressing the officer.

"They are, Mademoiselle."

"The ring is worth eight hundred dollars, and it is yours for eight minutes' private conversation with the prisoner."

"Impossible, Mademoiselle."

"Eight hundred dollars for eight minutes. That is at the rate of a hundred dollars a minute."

"True, Mademoiselle," replied the officer, "but if in those eight minutes my prisoner should take it into his head to jump out of that window, I am a ruined man."

"I pledge you my honour I will make no attempt to escape!" said Paul, eagerly.

The officer reflected for a few moments, and then looking searchingly into the face of the young Mexican, he said, energetically. "I have known many a gentleman pledge his word, and break it as if it was a bit of cracked china; but our profession teaches us to reckon up a man by the cut of his phiz, and I think you're an honourable man, Mr. Lisimon, and I don't think you guilty of this business that's brought against you, so give me the ring, Mademoiselle," he added, holding out his hand for the valuable trinket. "I'll step outside and wait while you say what you've got to say."

He walked out of the room and closed the door behind him, leaving Pauline and the Mexican together.

"Paul Lisimon, I come to save you," said Mademoiselle Corsi.

"You come from Camillia?"

"No; I come of my own accord. That ring is Camillia's, she gave it to me at my request, as a bribe for your gaoler."

"Noble girl!"

"Ay, noble girl!" exclaimed the Frenchwoman, bitterly: "because she gave one from the costly heaps of jewels her foolish father has lavished upon her; but I, whose brain devised the plan, deserve no word of praise."

"Pardon me, Mademoiselle Corsi, believe me I am not ungrateful."

"Paul Lisimon," said Pauline, fixing her limpid blue eyes upon the face of the Mexican, "you love Camillia Moraquitos?"

"Love her—?"

"Nay, why seek to dissemble? Do you think I have not read your shallow secret from the very first? You sought to blind and hoodwink me, but I laughed at the pitiful deception. Paul, tell me, is this love a lasting one?"

"Since you know my secret," replied the Mexican, "concealment is useless. It is a lasting love – eternal as yonder blue heaven."

"Foolish boy. Then ruin and destruction will track your footsteps."

"Ruin! Through my love?"

"Yes; you have not one friend in this house, save her who now speaks to you. Camillia loves you, you will answer! Yes; but with the feeble passion of a capricious beauty, which may change with to-morrow's sun. How long, think you, will her love endure when she hears every creature in New Orleans brand you as a thief and ingrate? Will it outlast the hour when she sees you placed in a criminal dock, side by side, with the lowest thief in the city? Will it survive degradation and shame? No; Camillia Moraquitos is proud, and from the hour that you leave this house with the clanking fetters on your wrists, she will despise and hate you – hate you for the very memory of her past love."

Paul Lisimon knew the pride which formed the leading principle in Camillia's character, and he felt that there might be truth in these bitter words.

"Oh, Heaven," he cried, "this is indeed terrible!"

"Hear me, Paul. It is in my power to save you from these fetters and this shame. It is in my power to bring Silas Craig and his haughty employer, Don Juan Moraquitos, grovelling to your feet to implore *you* for mercy – to entreat *your* forbearance to save them from the fate of a felon."

"You are mad!" exclaimed Paul. "What in mercy's name mean you by these words?"

"Listen to me, Paul Lisimon, for these few minutes, bought from the vigilance of the officer without yonder door, must decide the fate of both of us. Thirteen years ago, Don Tomaso Crivelli expired in the arms of his brother-in-law, in an apartment at the end of the gallery outside this door. You have often been in that room."

"I have. It is sacred to me, for it was there my earliest friend breathed his last sigh."

"That chamber is hung with Indian embroidery of shells and feathers upon leather. These hangings are about two feet from the wall, leaving an aperture behind large enough to admit of a slender person's hiding behind the embroidery. On the night of your benefactor's death *I* was concealed behind these hangings."

"You, a spy! But for what reason?"

"Don't doubt that I had my reason – reasons which at some future time I will reveal. When I carried the child Camillia to her uncle's bedside I heard a few words dropped which excited my curiosity; to gratify that curiosity I concealed myself at eleven o'clock that night behind the hangings of the dying man's bedchamber. There I heard Tomaso Crivelli dictate his last will and testament to the lawyer, Silas Craig, in the presence of your father. The signature to that will was afterwards witnessed by two persons, one a creature of the attorney's, the other a dependent of Don Juan Moraquitos."

"But what has all this to do with me?" asked Paul.

"It might have much to do with you. That night I learned a secret—"

"A secret!"

"Yes; and one by the aid of which I can save you from shame and humiliation, and elevate you to the proudest position even your haughty spirit could devise."

"You can do all this?"

"I can."

"And you will?"

"On one condition."

"That is—"

"That you renounce for ever all thoughts of Camillia Moraquitos; and that in the hour when, through my aid, you are elevated to name and fortune, you will make me your wife."

"You – my wife!" exclaimed Paul, thunderstruck by the words of the Frenchwoman.

"Yes. Is there anything so monstrous in the proposition? I am a few years older than you, it is true. I have not the Spanish beauty of

Camillia, but flattering tongues have told me that I am not destitute of the power to charm – I am no love-sick girl, but an ambitious woman, with a brain to scheme and plot a glorious future – I ask no love from you, but a share in the future to which I can elevate you. Do you refuse my offer?"

"I do," replied Paul. "Camillia Moraquitos may cast my image from her heart – may join with the rest and think me guilty; but, to the last, she, and she alone, will possess my love. Through the deepest abyss of shame and degradation I will be true to the guiding star of my life. Keep your secret, Mademoiselle Corsi; it can never be mine at the price which you propose."

"Fool!" cried the Frenchwoman, "you have refused rank, name, station, and wealth – nay, more than these, revenge! Be it so; abide by your choice. Perish in ignorance of the mighty secret which I have kept for thirteen patient years, and which will be a fortune to me if not to you. Rot in a gaol; die in a transport ship; drag out your life in a penal settlement; Pauline Corsi has spoken for the first and last time."

She walked to the door of the apartment, and, opening it, admitted the officer.

"You see," she said, "there has been no attempt at escape." Without one glance at Paul, she descended the staircase, and returned to the chamber in which she had left heart-broken Camillia.

That night Paul Lisimon was lodged in the gaol devoted to the reception of those accused of felony.

CHAPTER XIV.
AUGUSTUS HORTON TRIES TO AVENGE HIMSELF.

THE PARAGRAPH IN THE NEW ORLEANS PAPER

Upon the day following that on which the events occurred which we have described in the foregoing chapter, the Selma steamer started from New Orleans, laden with gay and fashionable company.

It was nine o'clock in the morning when the bell rang for the starting of the vessel – a gorgeous summer's day, the sky blue and cloudless, the Mississippi dancing in the sunshine.

Amongst the passengers on board the boat were Augustus Horton, his sister Adelaide, Mrs. Montresor, Silas Craig, and William Bowen.

This latter personage had exchanged his ragged skin-jacket and patched cotton shirt for a costume which aped that worn by the fops of New Orleans.

He followed close at the heels of Silas Craig, to the evident annoyance of the lawyer, who seemed, however, unable to shake him off.

Augustus and his party were bound for Hortonville, the plantation and villa of which we have already spoken, and which was situated upon the banks of the river, some miles beyond that belonging to Silas Craig.

The attorney was also bound for his plantation, whither he was taking William Bowen, who was henceforth to act as his overseer.

Augustus Horton was elated at the success of his villainous plot. He had lodged the only rival whom he feared in a felon's gaol; he felt that Camillia Moraquitos might now be easily won; but his heart – if the profligate who yields only to the dictates of passion can be said to have a heart – was full of the image of Cora, the Octoroon.

Just as the boat was about pushing off, two young men stepped on board. The first was Mortimer Percy, the second Gilbert Margrave, the young engineer and artist, who carried a sketch-book under his arm. He saluted Augustus and his sister with a grave bow of recognition.

"So! Gilbert," said Mortimer, "you come armed with your pencils and sketch-book, in order, I suppose, to catch some of the beauties of the Mississippi banks as we glide past them."

"To tell you the truth, my dear Mortimer, I have far graver reason for being here. I come to meet someone."

"A lady?"

"Yes."

"And her name is—?"

"Miss Cora Leslie."

"Good Heavens, my dear Gilbert, are you in earnest? You know this girl's history?"

"I do; and in my eyes that very history renders her even more sacred than a defenceless woman must ever be to the mind of an honourable man. I received a message this morning from Mr. Leslie's old slave, Toby, informing me that his young mistress is to come on board the boat at the first station, and begging me to be there to meet her, as she might have need of my services."

"And you took the hint?"

"Gladly – proudly."

"My dear Gilbert, I'm afraid you're very far gone," exclaimed Mortimer, laughing.

Adelaide Horton's heart sank as she received the young engineer's cold salutation. She felt that he despised both herself and her brother for their conduct to Cora. Mrs. Montresor and Adelaide soon withdrew to the saloon, for the sight of Gilbert Margrave was painful to the impetuous girl.

The scene on board the Selma was a gay and animated one. In the centre of the deck a German band was stationed, and every now and then some sprightly waltz or polka sounded on the summer air. Close against one of the paddle boxes a group of eager gamblers had seated themselves round a card-table, and it was amongst these that Mr. William Bowen planted himself, while Silas Craig conversed in an under-tone with Augustus Horton.

Gilbert Margrave and Mortimer Percy stood near the side of the vessel talking on indifferent subjects.

Presently the bell rang again, and the steamer stopped at the first station, which was situated at a short distance from Gerald Leslie's plantation.

"Miss Leslie knows nothing as yet of the fatal truth," said Gilbert. "I tremble lest she should ever learn it."

"Then tremble for her to-day on board this steamer," replied Mortimer, "these people know all, and they are pitiless."

"I shall be here to protect her, at the worst; but tell me have you any idea how it was that this mulatto Toby applied to me above all people?"

"The instincts of the despised race are strong," answered Mortimer; "he knew, no doubt, that you felt no uncommon interest in his young mistress. See, is not that Miss Leslie yonder, amongst the passengers, dressed in black?"

"It is; she is coming this way with Toby."

"I will leave you then, my dear Gilbert," said Mortimer, and pressing his friend's hand, he strolled into the saloon.

Cora Leslie was pale as a lily. Her black robes seemed to increase this almost unearthly pallor, but they could not take from her beauty. She advanced slowly, looking about her with a glance of terror, while the faithful mulatto followed close at her side. Presently she perceived Gilbert Margrave, who silently awaited her coming.

The crimson blush which suddenly dyed her cheek revealed how little she had expected this meeting.

"Mr. Margrave!" she exclaimed.

"Pardon me, Miss Leslie," replied the young engineer, "if I have ventured to make myself, without your permission, your companion upon this journey – but the hope that I might be able to render you some service has induced me even to brave your displeasure."

Cora looked earnestly at Toby; the faithful creature's eyelids fell beneath that searching gaze. "Ah, Mr. Margrave," she said, "it was Toby who told you of this journey?"

"Forgive me, dear young mistress," exclaimed the mulatto; "I thought that I was doing right."

"I am deeply affected with this proof of your kindness, Mr. Margrave," said Cora; "but I regret that Toby's indiscretion should have imposed upon you a task which will, as I believe, be useless."

"However that may be, Miss Leslie, it is a task which I accept with pride and joy."

At this moment the little group was approached by the captain of the Selma, whose sharp eyes had espied the dark skin of Toby amongst his aristocratic passengers.

"Hello! what are you doing here, nigger?" he exclaimed; "don't you know your place is at the other end of the vessel?"

The mulatto retired without a word, but not without a push from the indignant captain.

"Poor Toby," murmured Cora, as she followed with her eyes the faithful slave.

"You see, Miss Leslie," said Gilbert, "the company of Toby would have been no protection to you."

"I should have gone with him, Mr. Margrave. Is not my place his? Am I not an Octoroon?"

"You know all, then?"

"Yes. Alas! I see that it was only I who was ignorant."

"A chance word from Mr. Percy revealed the secret to me, Miss Leslie, upon that very night when first I saw you."

"Oh, Mr. Margrave, I do not seek to deny my origin. See, I wear mourning for my mother, and my journey of to-day is a pilgrimage to her grave."

A couple of chairs near Gilbert Margrave were unoccupied; one of these he offered to Cora, and, taking the other, seated himself by her side.

A noisy laugh from a group on deck at this moment arrested their attention.

This group was composed of Silas Craig, William Bowen, and two or three other passengers, all gathered round Augustus Horton, who was reading a paragraph aloud from a New Orleans newspaper. The following were the words which greeted Cora's ears–

"The conduct of Mr. Leslie in daring to foist the child of one of his slaves upon the highest circles of society, merits the punishment with which he has met. The citizens of New Orleans have shown their indignation at his offence, by abandoning all communication with him. Gerald Leslie walks the streets of his native city a stranger, and a ruined man."

"Oh, this is infamous," exclaimed Gilbert Margrave; "that man knows that you are here and he reads that paragraph on purpose to insult you. I will not endure it."

He was about to rush forward towards Augustus Horton, but Cora caught his arm in her slender hands and arrested his steps.

"For pity's sake," she cried; "for my sake, Mr. Margrave, not one word! The sting of the insult will be lost if it is unnoticed. Let him think those cruel words are unheard."

It was indeed as Gilbert Margrave had supposed. Augustus knew of Cora's presence in the boat – he had seen her with Gilbert by her side, and he was determined to be revenged upon her for the contempt with which she had treated him.

This was the planter's love. The love of the profligate who seeks to humiliate his victim in order that he may subdue her.

CHAPTER XV.
THE CHALLENGE.

THE DENUNCIATION

After Augustus Horton had read the paragraph in the New Orleans paper – a paragraph whose every line was calculated to wound the sensitive nature of the Octoroon – he looked towards Cora to see what effect the insult had had upon her and Gilbert Margrave.

They were seated side by side, and appeared engrossed in conversation, apparently unconscious of all that was passing around them. The planter threw down the newspaper with a smothered ejaculation of rage.

"Curse her!" he muttered; "is there no way to humble that proud soul? He, the Englishman, is by her side, deferential as if he were talking to a queen. No matter! My turn will come."

He withdrew to the saloon, with a crowd of friends and satellites, who flocked round him as one of the richest planters of Louisiana.

William Bowen had lost a handful of dollars at the gaming-table, and followed his patron, Silas Craig, in order to obtain a fresh supply from that gentleman.

The deck was therefore almost deserted. A few passengers, ladies and gentlemen, lounging here and there, upon the comfortable benches; the ladies employed in some elegant needlework, the gentlemen smoking; but Cora and Gilbert Margrave sat apart, and out of hearing of the rest.

"Tell me, Miss Leslie," said Gilbert, as Augustus Horton left the deck, "why did you prevent my inflicting upon that man the chastisement which he so richly deserved? Why did you compel me to remain silent, and suffer you to be insulted with impunity?"

"Because I would not have you resent that which, in Louisiana, is considered a justifiable prejudice. I pardon Augustus Horton as I pardon his sister, Adelaide, who was once my friend."

"Oh, do not speak of her, Miss Leslie, my contempt—"

"Nay, Mr. Margrave! it is you who are mistaken in all this. You are a stranger here, and your noble conduct of to-day may compromise you in the eyes of every colonist in Louisiana. Your place is not here by the side of me, an Octoroon; you should be with Adelaide Horton, a high-born daughter of the European race."

"If nobility of race is to be judged of by the elevation of the soul, it is you, and not Miss Horton, who can claim the loftiest birth," replied Gilbert, with emotion.

"You deceive yourself, Mr. Margrave," said Cora; "Adelaide has a generous heart, and I know that in secret she regrets our broken friendship – you, above all others, should be indulgent to her faults."

"I?"

"Yes," replied Cora, her long black eyelashes drooping beneath the Englishman's ardent gaze; "amongst all her English admirers, there was one alone for whom she felt any real regard. Do you know whom I mean?"

"No, Miss Leslie, nor do I wish to know," answered Gilbert, with energy; "for amongst all the young girls who adorned the farewell ball given by Mrs. Montresor, there was one and one alone to whom my dazzled eyes turned as the star of the brilliant throng. Do you know whom I mean?"

Cora did not answer, but a vivid blush suffused her face at the young engineer's question.

"See," continued Gilbert, opening his sketch-book; "do you remember the bouquet which you left upon a side table in the ante-room. In the centre of that bouquet bloomed this tiny blue flower, which we Englishmen call the forget-me-not. It is withered now. Say, Cora, can you forgive the hand which stole the blossom?"

The blush faded from the cheek of the Octoroon, and, clasping her hands entreatingly, she exclaimed with earnestness,–

"Oh, Mr. Margrave, reflect! An idle word, idly spoken, may occasion evil of which you cannot dream. It is to your honour I appeal! You would not inflict new sorrow upon a heart already almost broken. What would that flower say? that in its brief hour of bloom and freshness Cora Leslie was admired. The flower has withered, and the hopes of my life have faded like the frail petals of that poor blossom."

"No, Cora, no! The flower has but one meaning – it says, 'I love you!' "

"Me!" cried Cora, with an exclamation almost of terror. "But do you forget who I am? Do you forget that I am an Octoroon, the daughter of a slave?"

"I forget all, but that I love you."

"Do you not know that in this country it is considered a disgrace to bestow an honourable affection upon a creature of the despised race, and that the shame attached to me would attach itself also to you?"

"I know all, Cora, but I love you – I love you!" cried Gilbert, falling on his knees at the young girl's feet.

Cora sank into a chair and covered her face with her hands.

"Cora, you weep!"

"I do," she replied in faltering accents. "I feel myself so despised and abandoned in this cruel country; and it is so sweet to hear words of love and consolation from – from one –"

"Ah, Cora, speak – speak, I implore!"

"From one we love!"

"Cora, my adored," exclaimed Gilbert, with rapture, clasping her hand, and seating himself by her side.

They had not been unwatched during this interview. The eyes of jealousy were upon the unconscious lovers, for Adelaide Horton had emerged from the saloon, and, gliding at the back of the little table, had heard the latter part of their conversation.

She knew the worst now. This man – this man to whom she had given her heart, unasked and unsought, loved and was beloved by the despised daughter of a slave. Wounded pride, jealousy, revenge, humiliation, all mingled in the passionate emotion of that moment. Blind with anger, she knew not what she did.

By this time the deck of the Selma was again crowded with passengers. Augustus Horton still carried the New Orleans paper in his hand, and he was talking to Silas Craig about the attack upon Mr. Leslie.

"Confess now, you sly old fox," he said, laughing, "you are the author of this article? Why be too modest to own so good a work?"

Gilbert Margrave started from his seat.

"Now, Cora," he whispered, "I can no longer remain silent. I have now a right to defend you."

The captain of the Selma at this moment joined the group round Augustus Horton.

"You are talking of the article in the New Orleans *Messenger,* are you not, gentlemen?" he said.

"We are, Captain," replied Augustus, "and here is the author," he added, pointing to Craig.

"Then allow me to compliment you, sir!" said the Captain, addressing Silas. "You have done a service to society, and I hope the colonists will take warning."

"That they will never do," said Adelaide Horton, advancing to the centre of the group, "while you permit a mulattress to take her place on board your boat amongst the free citizens of New Orleans."

She pointed as she spoke to Cora, who had advanced with Gilbert Margrave.

There was a simultaneous movement of surprise amongst the passengers, as if a pistol had been suddenly fired upon the deck.

As Adelaide uttered these words, Mrs. Montresor and Mortimer Percy emerged from the saloon, and watched the scene which was taking place.

"What do you mean, Miss Horton?" asked the Captain.

"Oh! Adelaide, Adelaide," murmured Mortimer, "this is indeed despicable!"

Terrified at and ashamed of what she had done, the jealous girl hid her face in her hands and retired rapidly from the deck, followed by her aunt.

"I will tell you, sir, what Miss Horton meant," said Cora, advancing to the Captain; "she would have told you that I am Gerald Leslie's daughter."

"In that case, madam," replied the Captain, "you must be aware—"

"That my place is with the slaves at the other end of the steamer. Pardon me, sir, for having forgotten my real position!"

With one proudly disdainful glance at Augustus Horton, Cora slowly retired. The passengers watched her in silence, wondering how the strange scene would end.

Gilbert Margrave advanced to Augustus Horton, and addressed him in a tone of quiet determination, far more impressive than the loudest passion.

"Mr. Horton," he said; "the insult inflicted upon Miss Leslie was offered also to me, since I was by her side at the time. Whether her cause be just or unjust, I insist – you understand, Sir, – I insist upon an immediate reparation for an act which I consider an abominable cowardice."

"As you please, sir," replied the planter. "I shall land at Iberville."

"Enough. I also will land there."

"Why not throw the Englishman overboard?" said Craig, in an undertone to some of the passengers.

Augustus Horton overheard the words, and turned fiercely upon the lawyer –

"I allow no interference in this," he said; "the quarrel is mine alone. Percy, you will be my second?"

"Pardon me," replied Mortimer Percy, "as Mr. Margrave is a stranger in Louisiana, he may have difficulty in finding any one to assist him in this matter. You will excuse me, therefore, if I give him the preference."

"As you please," answered Augustus, indifferently.

Gilbert grasped the hand of his old friend; "Thanks, Mortimer," he whispered, "your heart is generous as ever."

"Perhaps you won't mind having me for a second, Mr. Horton," said William Bowen; "I'm rather an old hand in these sort of affairs."

Augustus glanced at him with one brief look of contempt, but replied, after a pause, "Be it so, Mr. Bowen; I accept your services. This evening, then, Mr. Margrave. We meet at sunset, in the wood on the borders of Mr. Craig's plantation at Iberville."

"We shall be punctual," answered Gilbert.

CHAPTER XVI.
CAPTAIN PRENDERGIILLS OF THE AMAZON.

While the Selma steamed proudly past the banks of the Mississippi, the inhabitants of New Orleans were occupied by the discussion of an event which had taken place on the previous night, but which had only been discovered early that morning.

Paul Lisimon had escaped from prison.

When Silas Craig and Augustus Horton took their places on board the Selma, they little dreamed that their victim had escaped them.

Nevertheless it was so. The turnkey who visited the cell occupied by the young Mexican at eight o'clock on the morning after his arrest, found, to his bewilderment, that the dreary apartment was empty. The bars of the narrow window had been cut away, and a file, left upon the floor of the cell, told of patient labour which had occupied the prisoner in the silence of the night.

A rope, one end of which was attached to the stump of one of the bars, also told of the mode of escape.

One thing was sufficiently clear. Paul Lisimon had received assistance from without. He had been searched upon his entrance into the prison, and nothing of a suspicious character had been found about him; the file and rope had, therefore, been conveyed to him by some mysterious hand.

The astonished officials of the gaol looked from one to the other, not knowing what to suspect.

The escape seemed almost incredible; for, in order to regain his liberty, the prisoner had not only to descend from the window of his cell, which was thirty feet above the prison yard, but he had also to scale the outer wall, which was upwards of twenty feet high, and surmounted by a formidable *chevaux de frise*.

How, then, had Paul Lisimon accomplished a feat hitherto unattempted by the most daring of criminals?

None suspected the truth of the matter. None could guess at the real clue to the mystery!

Paul Lisimon had neither descended from the window of his cell, nor scaled the outer wall of the prison. He had walked out of the gaol in the silence and darkness of the night, and in five minutes from leaving his cell had found himself in the streets of New Orleans.

The person who had effected this miraculous escape was no other than the gaoler, who had charge of Lisimon; and this gaoler was one of the most trusted functionaries of the prison. Sir Robert Walpole said that every man has his price: this man had been richly bribed by a mysterious visitor, who had gained admission to the gaol on the evening of Paul's arrest.

The rope and the file had been used in order to blind the governor of the prison to the real delinquent.

At daybreak on the morning after his imprisonment, Paul Lisimon found himself free in the streets of New Orleans, but utterly ignorant as to the mysterious being to whom he owed his release.

The gaoler had refused to give him any information about this person.

"I know nothing of the business," the man said, "except that I am well paid for my share in it, and that I shall be a ruined man if I am found out."

Paul Lisimon was free!

He was free; but he stood alone in the world, without a friend – branded as a thief – cast off by the protector of his youth – an escaped felon!

He hurried towards the lonely and deserted quay. Despair was in his heart, and he yearned to rest beneath the still waters of the Mississippi.

"There, at least," he murmured, "I shall be at peace. Camillia now believes me innocent, and she will weep for my memory. Were I to await the issue of a trial, which must result in shame and condemnation, she might indeed, as that Frenchwoman insinuated, learn to despise me."

Heedless of all around him, absorbed in gloomy meditation, Paul Lisimon was for some time unaware of the sound of a footfall close behind him; but as he drew nearer to the water side this footstep approached him still closer, and presently, in the faint grey light of that mysterious hour, betwixt night and morning, he beheld the long shadow of a man's figure upon the ground beside him.

He started and turned round. As he did so, a heavy hand was laid upon his shoulder, and a deep bass voice exclaimed,–

"What do you want with yonder dark water, my lad, that you're in such a hurry to get to the river side?"

Paul shook the man's hand away from his shoulder with a gesture of anger. "By what right do you question me?" he said; "stand aside, and let me pass!"

"Not till we've had a few words, my gaol bird," answered the stranger.

"Gaol bird!"

"Yes, mate, gaol bird! you've no need to carry it off so fiercely with me. A file and a rope, eh? to blind the governor of the prison, and a good-natured turnkey to open the doors for you. That's about the sort of thing, isn't it?"

Paul Lisimon turned round, and looked the stranger full in the face. He was a big, broad-shouldered fellow, upwards of six feet high, dressed in a thick pilot coat, and immense leather boots, which came above his knees. The pilot coat was open at the waist, and in the uncertain glimmer of the morning light Paul Lisimon caught sight of the butt end of a pistol thrust into a leather belt. The stranger's face had once been a handsome one, but it bore upon it the traces of many a debauch, as well as the broad scar of a cutlass wound, which had left a deep welt from cheek to chin.

"I know not who you are," said Paul, after looking long and earnestly at this man, "nor by what right you have interested yourself in my fate; but it is evident to me that you have had some hand in my miraculous escape of to-night."

"Never mind that, comrade," answered the stranger, linking his arm in that of Paul Lisimon, and walking slowly toward the quay. "You're free and welcome, as far as that goes; but I don't think, after an old friend had taken a good bit of trouble to get you out of that thundering gaol yonder – I don't think it was quite fair to go and try to chuck yourself into the water."

"You, then, were my deliverer?"

"Never you mind whether I was or whether I wasn't. Do you know what it cost to get you out of prison?"

"No."

"Well, near upon a thousand dollars, my lad."

"And you paid this money! You, an utter stranger to me, bribed my gaolers!"

"Never you mind about that, I say again; those that paid the money for you didn't grudge a farthing of it. As to being a stranger, perhaps I'm not quite that."

"You know me, then?"

"Fifteen years ago I knew a little, curly-haired, black-eyed chap, who used to play about the gardens of a white-walled villa on the banks of the Amazon, and I fancy that you and he are pretty near relations."

"You knew me in my childhood; you knew me in the lifetime of my earliest and dearest benefactor."

"I did. It was only last night that I came ashore, and the first thing I heard in New Orleans was that Mr. Paul Lisimon had been arrested for the robbery of his employer, one of the land sharks your genteel folks call lawyers. Now, we seamen are not over fond of that breed, so I wasn't sorry to hear that for once a lawyer had been robbed himself, instead of robbing other people, so I asked who this Paul Lisimon was that had been too many guns for his employer, and they told me that he was a young Mexican, who had been brought up by Don Juan Moraquitos. Now, I happen to know a good deal of Don Juan Moraquitos, and I had never heard before of Paul Lisimon; but I had heard of a little curly haired lad that was once a great favourite with Don Tomaso Crivelli, and Don Tomaso had been a good friend to me. So that's why your gaoler was bribed, and why you stand a free man in the streets of New Orleans this morning."

"My generous friend," exclaimed Paul, "this is all so much a mystery to me that I know not how to thank you for your goodness."

"And I tell you that I want no thanks, so let's talk of business. In the first place what made you so anxious to get to the water just now? I thought there was blood in your veins that never yet ran in those of a coward."

"A coward?"

"Ay, youngster; the man who has no better resource when he's down in the world than to make away with himself isn't worthy of any other name."

"And what right had you to suppose that I contemplated suicide?"

"The right of a good sharp pair of eyes, my lad. But come, once more to business. Do you see yonder craft at anchor there, to the right of the harbour?"

Paul looked in the direction to which the stranger pointed, and perceived the trim masts of a lightly built schooner.

"I do."

"Then you see one of the fastest clippers that ever sailed. No rotten timber, but green oak and locust from stem to stern, with not an inch of canvas that isn't meant for speed. Don't talk to me about your steam vessels; lumbering old Noah's arks, that can't go a good pace without bursting up and sending every soul to tarnation smash. See the Amazon fly before the wind, and then you'll know what fast sailing is. If we Southerners come to handy grips with the North, let the Yankees look out for squalls when the Amazon is afloat on the blue water."

"And you, my friend, are you one of her crew?" asked Paul.

"I'm her captain, mate, Captain Prendergills – a sailor by profession, a rover by choice, and a privateer for plunder."

"A privateer?"

"Yes. You don't think the word an ugly one, do you? Now listen to me; you can't go back to Villa Moraquitos, can you?"

"No."

"And you and Don Juan have parted company for a long spell?"

"We have."

"Very well, then, why not join us? I may have more reasons than one for taking an interest in you. You can't stay in New Orleans, for by eight o'clock this morning your escape will be discovered. I've a fancy that you'd make a smart mate on board yonder vessel. Will you come?"

"I will," answered Paul, grasping his new friend by the hand. "You at least trust me – you do not fear to take me on board your vessel, though the hand of suspicion is upon me, and men have called me thief. Providence seems to have raised you up, as if by a miracle, to preserve me from disgrace, despair, and death. I am yours for good or evil; in weal or woe I will serve you faithfully."

CHAPTER XVII.
REVELATIONS OF GUILT.

Don Juan Moraquitos was one of the first to hear of the escape of Paul Lisimon. The reader must remember that the Spaniard knew nothing of the infamous plot devised by Silas Craig at the instigation of Augustus Horton. He believed his protégé to be guilty of the crime imputed to him.

He had a secret reason for rejoicing in the disgrace of the young Mexican, and he had a still stronger motive in seeking the destruction of

Paul, since he had begun to suspect the attachment between Lisimon and Camillia.

He hurried to his daughter's apartment, in order to inform her of Paul's escape from prison.

"Now, Camillia, what think you of this haughty youth who so proudly declared his innocence?" said Don Juan, after relating the account he had just heard of Lisimon's escape.

"I think as I have ever thought," answered Camillia.

"That he is innocent?"

"Yes!" replied the Spanish girl.

"Strange, then, that he should have fled," said Don Juan; "the innocent man generally awaits to meet the issue of his trial; it is only the guilty wretch who flies to hide himself from the avenging power of the law he has outraged."

Pauline Corsi had been present during this brief dialogue, but she had remained silent, with her fingers busy with the rainbow silks of her embroidery, and her eyes bent over her work. She raised them, however, as the Spaniard uttered these words and looked him full in the face.

"The guilty do not always fly, Don Juan Moraquitos," she said quietly.

The Spaniard started and looked at Mademoiselle Corsi with a rapid, but furtive glance.

"They sometimes remain for years upon the scene of their guilt. They defy the laws which they have outraged, and triumph in their undiscovered and successful villainy."

Don Juan laughed mockingly, but a close observer might have detected an uneasy quiver of his mustachio-shaded lip.

"Mademoiselle Corsi appears to speak from experience," he said. "She has perhaps known such people?"

"I *have* known such people," answered the Frenchwoman in the same quiet tone in which she had first addressed Don Juan.

"They could scarcely be desirable acquaintances for the instructress of—"

"The daughter of so honourable a man as yourself, Don Juan," said Pauline, as if interpreting the thoughts of her employer.

While this conversation was going forward between Mademoiselle Corsi and the Spaniard, Camillia Moraquitos had strolled out on to the balcony, to escape the watchful eyes of her father, and to conceal the relief she felt in her lover's escape. Pauline and Don Juan were, therefore, alone. Their eyes met. There was something in the glance of the Frenchwoman which told plainly that her words had no common meaning.

For some moments the gaze of Don Juan was rooted upon that fair face and those clear and radiant blue eyes – a face which was almost childlike in its delicacy and freshness, and which yet, to the experienced eye of the physiognomist, revealed a nature rarely matched for intelligence and cunning.

Don Juan crossed the apartment to the curtained recess in which Pauline Corsi was seated, and, placing himself in the chair opposite to her, grasped her slender wrist in his muscular hand.

"There is a hidden significance in your words," he said.

"Can you not read their meaning, Don Juan?"

"No."

"You cannot?"

"I cannot," he answered defiantly.

"Say rather that you will not," replied the Frenchwoman, scornfully. "You fear to commit yourself by an avowal which may seem like a confession of guilt. Shall I tell you the meaning of those words?"

"Yes."

"You are a brave man, Don Juan Moraquitos, you do not fear to hear the truth?"

"I do not."

"Then listen to me. Those words have relation to an event which occurred thirteen years ago!"

"My memory is no longer that of a young man," answered Don Juan; "I cannot remember all the events which happened at that date."

"Perhaps not; but you can remember the death of your kinsman, Don Tomaso Crivelli?"

This time the Spaniard started as if an adder had stung him. The cold perspiration broke out upon his bronzed forehead, and every vestige of colour fled alike from cheek and lips.

"I see you *do* remember," said Pauline Corsi. "You remember the will which was made on that night. The will which was witnessed by two men; one of them a seafaring man whose name I know not as yet; the other, William Bowen, then captain of a slaver. You remember the sick man's confession. You remember his dying prayer, that those dear to him should be protected by you; and lastly, Don Juan Moraquitos, you remember the draught mixed by Silas Craig, and which your wife's brother, Tomaso Crivelli, took from *your* hand, two hours before his death!"

"How could you have learnt all this?" gasped the Spaniard.

"I know more than this!" replied Pauline Corsi. "When the faint grey of the wintry dawn was stealing through the half-open shutters of the sick chamber, Tomaso Crivelli lifted himself from his pillow in the last agonies of death, and uttered an accusation—"

"Hold! hold, woman, I entreat!" cried the Spaniard, "you know all! How you have acquired that knowledge, save through some diabolical agency, I know not; for the door of the chamber was secured by a lock not easily tampered with, and those within were not the men to betray secrets. But, no matter, you know all! Why have you kept silence for thirteen years?"

"We women are tacticians, Don Juan. I had a motive for my silence!"

"And you speak now—?"

"Because I think it is the right time to speak."

Don Juan paced the apartment backwards and forwards with folded arms, and his head bent upon his breast. Presently pausing before Pauline Corsi's embroidery frame, he said in a hoarse whisper,

"Do you mean to betray me?"

"No!"

"Why then tell me all this?"

"Because I would ask the reward of thirteen years' silence."

"And that reward—?"

"Is easy for you to grant. I am tired of dependence, even on *your* goodness. Make me your wife, and let me share the wealth acquired by the guilt of whose secrets I know."

CHAPTER XVIII.
THE DUEL IN THE MOONLIGHT.

THE MOMENT OF SUSPENSE

The plantation of Silas Craig, at Iberville, was situated, as we have already said, upon the borders of a wood; a luxuriant forest, stretching for miles upon the banks of the Mississippi, varied every here and there by undulating dells and pools of water, lying hidden beneath the shadows of giant trees, whose branches had waved for centuries above a solitude, broken only by the fleet foot of the Indian.

It was in this forest that the unhappy and martyred Quadroon, Francilia, lay in her quiet grave – a grassy mound, marked only by the rude wooden cross erected at its head by the faithful mulatto, Toby.

Here, at least, the lovely child of an accursed and trampled race was free. Here no master dared molest her tranquil slumber. Death sets the slave and the prisoner alike at liberty.

The red sun sank in crimson splendour beneath the purple waters of the mighty river; upon every forest tree gleamed golden reflections of the dying light; upon the bosom of each quiet pool the last sunbeams faded and flickered in the shadowy twilight, while, calmly beautiful, the moon arose in her tranquil glory, bathing forest and river in a hood of silvery radiance.

The last glimmer of crimson light was slowly fading as two men advanced through one of the pathways of the wood – a pathway so over-arched by the rich spreading branches of the trees, that it seemed one verdant arcade.

Each of these men carried a carbine upon his shoulder, and a powder flask slung at his side.

The first was William Bowen, the second, who closely followed his companion, was Augustus Horton. They emerged from the arcade into an open piece of turf, around which the trunks of the giant trees formed a species of a wall.

"Where, in the name of all that's diabolical, are you leading me, Bill?" said Augustus, looking about him.

"I guess you don't know your way in this here wood by moonlight, Mr. Horton," answered Bill Bowen, laughing; "but we're all right for all that. This is the spot where we appointed to meet that young Englishman and your precious cousin, Mr. Mortimer Percy, who ought to be ashamed of himself for taking the Britisher's part against his own countryman, and against his own flesh and blood, too, as far as that goes."

"Curse him!" muttered Augustus, between his teeth.

"Curse him, and welcome, sir, for my part – but this is where we promised to meet him and his friend. We're close against Craig's plantation. You could see the nigger huts through the trees if the leaves weren't so tarnation thick."

"Hark!" said the young planter; "what's that?"

The rustling of the leaves announced the arrival of the two men for whom they waited. They approached by the same pathway as that by which Augustus and Bill had come.

"What's that?" echoed Bowen; "why, it's your cousin and his friend, I guess; so keep your powder dry."

Mortimer Percy and Gilbert Margrave drew near them as William Bowen spoke. The four men bowed stiffly to each other.

"I fear that we have kept you waiting," said Mortimer. "We lost our way in the dusk, and have wasted ten minutes in finding it."

"Bowen and I have only just arrived," answered Augustus. "Have you brought your own weapons?"

"We couldn't get a pair of duelling pistols in the neighbourhood," replied Percy; "but I have brought a case of revolvers."

"Revolvers be hanged!" cried Bowen, advancing between Augustus Horton and his cousin. "I'll tell you what it is, gentlemen; the best thing you can do is to fight with these here carbines – neither of which ever missed fire since they came out of the gunmaker's hands. See yonder!" he added, pointing to a circular dell, shut in by the trees which sheltered it, and light as day in the broad moonbeams; "see there, gentlemen, yonder bit of ground ain't above a hundred feet broad, take it which way you will, so my advice is this, take up your stand on each side of the circle, and at a given signal advance upon each other. That'll give your duel the additional charm of the chase. What say you?"

"You forget," said Mr. Mortimer; "Mr. Margrave does not know the ground."

"Then we are perfectly equal upon that point," replied Augustus Horton; "for Bowen will tell you that I never set foot here until to-night."

"Come, gentlemen," cried Bill, impatiently, "is it agreed?"

"It is!" answered Gilbert Margrave and Mortimer Percy.

"Then choose your weapon," said Bowen, handing Mortimer the two carbines.

The young man carefully measured the instruments of death, and returned one to his cousin's second.

"Are they loaded?" he asked.

"No," answered Bowen, handing him powder and ball. "Will you remain on this side of the ground?"

"Yes."

"Good! then it is for you to cross over to the other side of yonder dell, I guess. Mr. Horton, come!"

"But the signal?" exclaimed Mortimer.

"Shall be a shout from me," answered Bowen; "we'll give you ten minutes to load your weapon and bid your friend good-bye, for if Mr. Horton's anything as good a shot as I take him for, there ain't much chance of your seeing the Britisher again!"

The two men disappeared amongst the foliage, and the friends were alone.

"Miss Leslie knows nothing of this duel, I suppose?" said Mortimer, busy loading the carbine.

"Nothing!" answered Gilbert. "Poor girl, I allowed her to believe that, for her sake, I had renounced all thought of vengeance upon the man who had insulted her!"

"Perhaps that's the wisest thing you could have done; for however this affair may terminate, I fear it will be a troublesome business for you. Men's minds are strangely excited just now; the Southern blood is up, and should you escape safe and sound from this duel, I doubt but you will have to secure the protection of the British consul to save you from the fury of the populace. Once sheltered by the dreaded flag of old England, neither North nor South dare touch a hair of your head; for if they should assail you, it would be the kindling of such a storm as would blot the stars and stripes of America from the universe."

"When a man sees a woman he loves insulted by a coward, he does not stop to reason," answered Gilbert; "the only thing that distresses me in this matter, is the thought that, instead of protecting my adored Cora,

I have only brought upon her new dangers. You are the only man in America whom I call my friend. You have already given me such powerful proofs of your friendship, that I think I may venture to demand of you one last service."

"Speak, Gilbert, speak. We have indeed been fast and faithful friends; to-night, above all other nights, I can refuse you nothing."

"Listen, then. My first care on leaving the Selma, was to engage a boat, which is to carry us back to Lake Pont Chartrain this very night. Promise me, that if I fall, you will yourself protect Cora, and restore her to her father's arms?"

"I promise," answered Mortimer, fervently.

"Thanks, thanks!"

The two men shook hands, both too much affected for many words.

"But tell me, Gilbert," said Mortimer Percy, after a pause, "what was Miss Leslie's motive for coming to Iberville?"

"Her mother died here. She comes to pay her first visit to the lonely grave of Francilia, the Quadroon."

"Ah! I understand. Poor girl, poor girl!"

"I left her with the mulatto, Toby, who was to conduct her to the spot. At ten o'clock she will return to the landing place on the river, where the boat will wait for us."

"Enough," said Mortimer, in a voice broken by emotion, "whatever happens I will be there to protect her."

At this moment a loud shout resounded through the stillness of the forest scene.

It was the signal.

"Take your weapon, Gilbert," said Mortimer, placing the carbine in Margrave's hand. "Augustus Horton is my cousin – you are my friend. I dare not pray for the safety of either, at the cost of the other's death. The moonlit heavens are shining down upon us, and the eye of Providence watches the struggle. Farewell!"

They clasped each other's hands once more in silence. Then Gilbert Margrave dashed forward through the brushwood, and disappeared in the dell below.

Mortimer Percy paced up and down the dewy turf, listening for the report of their guns.

"What is this?" he exclaimed, as he laid his hand upon his beating heart. "For which of these two men do I tremble? This, then, is America, of whose freedom her citizens so proudly boast! Here are two men met together to shed each other's blood, because one of them has dared to uphold the cause of a daughter of the despised race. Hark!"

It was for the report of the firearms that he listened, but the sound which met his ear was of altogether a different nature. It was the evening chorus of the negroes, floating upon the tranquil air. A sweet harmonious strain of melody, which breathed of peace and repose:-

"Day is dying, day is gone,
Weary niggers, rest;
Work all day, and toil and moan,
Quiet night is best!"

"Poor fellows," said Mortimer, "they are Craig's negroes, returning to their cabins after the day's labour. They sing, poor simple creatures. The overseer's lash cannot destroy the quiet content of their honest hearts. How easily might a good master make them happy."

Again the voices rise upon the balmy air:-

"Far from home, and child, and wife,
Weary niggers, weep,
Day goes by in toil and strife,
Night brings peace and sleep."

The voices slowly died away in the distance, echoing mournfully through the woodland glades, as the negroes passed out of hearing.

Mortimer Percy still listened – eagerly, breathlessly – for that other awful sound which would announce the commencement of the combat.

"Nothing yet!" he exclaimed; "If I turn the corner of yonder group of trees I run the chance of being struck by a random bullet; but come the worst, I must risk it, I can endure this suspense no longer."

He sprang through the forest growth in the same direction as that taken by Gilbert Margrave.

. He had not disappeared above three minutes when from the opposite side of the wood two figures slowly approached, casting long shadows on the moonlit grass.

The first was a man, the second a woman. It was the mulatto slave, Toby, who came hither to lead the Octoroon to her mother's grave.

"That song which you heard just now, Miss Cora, has been sung many a night above your cradle to lull you to sleep."

"My mother sang it?" exclaimed Cora.

"She did, she did! The sound of that song, my lady, will bring tears to Toby's eyes until the hour when they close in death."

"Faithful friend!"

"You are sad, dear mistress, you are uneasy?" said the mulatto. The intense watchfulness of the slave's affection enabled him to detect every varying shade in Cora's manner. He saw that her mind was disturbed by some anxiety.

"I am anxious about Mr. Margrave, Toby," she replied; "he promised to rejoin us ere this."

"The English gentleman may have had some difficulty in engaging a boat, dear mistress. You have seen the poor cabin in which your mother passed the two last months of her life. It is near this spot she reposes."

The slave looked about him in the moonlight, and presently paused at the foot of an enormous oak. Pushing aside the wild overgrowth which obscured it, he revealed a rough-hewn wood cross surmounting a humble mound of earth, which had been neatly turfed by the same faithful hand that had erected this simple monument.

Upon the cross this inscription had been carved in letters cut deep into the wood:–

"FRANCILIA. July 7th, 1845."

Below this name and date were three words. Those words were:

"BLOOD FOR BLOOD."

"See, Miss Cora," said the mulatto, "this is a lonely spot, though so near to the plantation. Few ever come here, for yonder dell is said to be haunted by the spirit of an Indian who was cruelly murdered there a hundred years ago. No hand has disturbed this cross.

"It may be that no human eye has ever seen the inscription, but the all-seeing eye of Providence has looked upon these words for fifteen weary years."

"Oh, spirit of my murdered mother!" exclaimed the young girl, lifting her clasped hands toward the effulgent sky. "Spirit of the unhappy and injured one, look down upon your daughter! May heaven forgive the sins of him who caused thy unhappy fate. May Heaven pity and pardon my wretched father. I cannot curse him. Here on the grave of his victim, on the grave of a victim of a wicked and cruel prejudice, I pity and forgive him, for he needs all pity, since he has sinned."

At this moment the report of a gun sounded in the dell near at hand. Cora rose suddenly from her knees, pale and terrified. "Toby," she cried, "Toby, did you hear?"

Before the mulatto could reply, Mortimer Percy sprang through the parted branches that bordered the dell, and rushed towards where they stood. He recoiled upon seeing Cora.

"You here, Miss Leslie!" he exclaimed.

"Yes, yes. Tell me, what was that report?"

"That! Some – some hunter, no doubt."

He had scarcely spoken when a second gun was fired.

"No, no, Mr. Percy!" cried Cora, wildly, "it is no hunter's carbine. A woman's unfailing instinct tells me of danger to him I love. Gilbert Margrave has been fighting a duel with your cousin."

Augustus Horton appeared as she spoke, walking backwards and gazing intently into the dell.

"I must have surely hit him," he muttered.

"See, see!" cried Cora, "his antagonist is safe. It is he who has fallen. Run, Toby, run to succour him."

Half fainting with terror and anguish, she would have fallen to the ground had not Mortimer's extended arm caught her in time. He carried her prostrate form to a rocky seat close at hand, on which she rested with her head still lying on his shoulder.

Augustus Horton advanced towards them, and recognised the Octoroon in the moonlight.

"She here!" he cried. "Cora!"

The passionate love of his guilty heart returned as he gazed upon the unconscious girl, and a thrill of jealousy vibrated through the dark recesses of his soul, as he beheld the lovely head of the Octoroon resting upon Mortimer's shoulder.

"I am not surprised, Percy, at your sympathy for Gerald Leslie's daughter," he said, with a sneer; "she is, of course, one of your friends, for she dared to turn me out of her house, dismissing me from her presence as if she had been a queen."

"You!" exclaimed Percy.

"Yes," replied his cousin, "because I had the impertinence to pay her a few idle compliments."

"Augustus Horton," said Mortimer, gravely, "you remember a clause in our contract of partnership, which provides for the agreement being cancelled at pleasure, by either of the two partners?"

"I do."

"Then I am the first to cancel that bond. From this night I cease to be your partner."

"So be it!" replied Augustus. "It is not for me to object to such a proposal, but have a care, Mortimer, and remember that by such a proceeding you lose half your estate."

"I shall have enough left to enable me to live far from a country which I henceforth renounce. As to your sister, you can tell her that I restore her her liberty."

"That is needless," answered Augustus, haughtily, "for she herself has declared her intention of breaking with you for ever."

"How?"

"She has presumed to fall in love with Mr. Gilbert Margrave, the gentleman who prefers an Octoroon to the heiress of one of the proudest families in Louisiana."

"It was jealousy, then, that prompted her denunciation of Cora Leslie," said Mortimer.

"It was."

"So much the better for her. That, at least, is some excuse for her conduct. Hush! here they come."

Bill Bowen and the mulatto appeared, as Percy spoke, carrying between them the prostrate form of Gilbert Margrave. The young man was quite unconscious, the breast of his shirt dyed crimson by the blood which welled from his wound. Toby and Bowen placed him upon the rocky seat which had been occupied by Cora.

"The ball has struck him in the side," said Bowen. "I guess it's about all over with the Britisher."

At the sound of these words of evil import, Cora Leslie opened her eyes, and, beholding the bleeding and prostrate form of her lover, flung herself on her knees at his feet.

"Gilbert, Gilbert!" she cried; "dead! and I am the cause of this."

The mulatto placed his hand upon the breast of the wounded man.

"The heart beats, though faintly," he said; "dear mistress, he will be saved."

"Will you allow him to be carried to your father's villa, Miss Leslie?" said Mortimer; "I will accompany you thither."

"Ah, Mr. Percy," exclaimed Cora, "you are all goodness."

"A hundred dollars for your trouble, Bowen, if you'll assist us in carrying this poor fellow to the boat," said Mortimer.

"A hundred dollars – I'm your man!" replied the American. "You'll excuse me, Mr. Horton, business is business, you know," he added, to Augustus.

Mortimer Percy and the mulatto gathered together several strong branches from the fallen wood lying beneath the trees, and twisted them into a rude litter on which they laid the unconscious Englishman.

One end of this litter was carried by Toby, the other by William Bowen; Cora and Mortimer walking by the side of the wounded man.

In this order they started for the landing-place, where Gilbert's boat was to await them.

Augustus Horton stood for some minutes watching their receding figures in the moonlight.

"My curses on them," he muttered; "I thought to-night's business would have settled for my proud Cora's English lover, and I have but favoured my rival's chance by what I have done. If this Gilbert Margrave should recover, of course he will be all love and gratitude for his beautiful nurse, who will watch and tend him in his hour of danger. But, no matter, Craig and I have a powerful hold on Gerald Leslie, and his daughter's love shall be the price of his safety. She would not like to see her father penniless. Or, if to the last she refuses to hear reason, the public auction will soon settle her scruples. If I cannot win her as my mistress, I can, at least, buy her as – my slave!"

CHAPTER XIX.
THE HUMAN BLOODHOUND.

The morning after the duel, Augustus Horton returned to New Orleans. Even in his jealousy of Gilbert Margrave and his guilty passion for the beautiful Octoroon, he did not abandon the thought of more ambitious schemes; and he was still determined to win the hand and the fortune of Camillia Moraquitos.

The first intelligence that greeted him on his return was the news of Paul Lisimon's escape from prison.

The planter was furious. This dreaded rival was, then, at liberty. The trial, which was to have ended in his disgrace and condemnation, would, perhaps, never take place, and Camillia might still believe in the honour and honesty of her lover.

That which he sought was to render Paul utterly contemptible in the sight of the haughty Spanish girl, and he felt that he had, in a great measure, failed.

He dispatched a special messenger to Iberville with a letter for Silas Craig, informing him of the young Mexican's escape.

"Lose no time in returning to New Orleans," he wrote. "I need the help of your craft in this business. There must be some mystery in this Lisimon's escape, and you are the man to unravel it."

This done, he ordered his horse, and, attended by his groom, rode at once to Villa Moraquitos. He was determined to precipitate matters, and enlist the Spaniard in his behalf. This he knew would be an easy matter, as Don Juan had always encouraged his addresses.

Augustus Horton found the Spaniard alone in an apartment, which was called his study, though little trace of studious habits was to be found within its walls.

The panelling of this chamber was adorned with weapons of every kind, arranged in symmetrical order upon the walls. Cutlasses, pistols, and carbines, of polished steel, inlaid with gold and enamel, hung in glittering array, side by side with charts of that ocean upon which, if scandalous tongues were correct, Don Juan Moraquitos had for many years been a rover.

When Augustus Horton entered this room the Spaniard was standing near the open window, his arms folded, his head bent upon his breast, moodily puffing a cheroot. He started as his visitor was announced, and, recovering himself as if by an effort, advanced to greet him.

"This is kind, my dear Augustus," he said, "but I thought you had left New Orleans for Hortonville."

"It is quite true – I left yesterday."

"And returned this morning?"

"Yes."

"Capricious boy! So soon tired of your rural retreat?"

"You cannot guess the cause of my return?"

"No, indeed!"

"What, Don Juan! Can you not imagine that there may be a lode-star shining in this city, which draws me back to it in spite of myself?"

"Ah! I begin to understand. And that lode-star is—"

"Your daughter, Camillia Moraquitos."

The Spaniard was silent for some moments, as if absorbed in thought. Then, turning to the planter, he said, gravely, "Augustus Horton, I have long foreseen this. I will freely own to you, that some time since, I cherished more ambitious views for my only child. We Spaniards are a proud race, and I once hoped that the husband of my daughter might be one of the haughty nobles of my distant native land. But that is past now," he added, with a sigh; "your rank is as high as that of any man in Louisiana. You are no penniless adventurer who seeks to enrich himself by marriage. You are young, handsome, wealthy. Win her then, you have my free consent."

"And your assistance?"

"Yes."

"But if she should refuse?"

"I cannot force her wishes. She is my only child, the sole treasure of an old man's heart. If you cannot win her love, you must submit to her refusal of your hand."

Augustus Horton retired with many expressions of gratitude and affection, but once outside the chamber his brow darkened and he clenched his fist as he muttered with an oath:–

"This Spaniard is like some foolish old woman. He cannot force his daughter's wishes, forsooth; and the double fortune of Don Juan Moraquitos and Don Tomaso Crivelli may go to any handsome adventurer upon whom Donna Camillia chooses to bestow her affection."

As these thoughts were busy in his brain, he crossed the spacious hall on his way to Camillia's apartments.

In the corridor leading to the young girl's boudoir he met Pauline Corsi.

He did not stop to speak to her, but passed her with a careless bow – such a salute as a man only bestows upon one whom he thinks far beneath him.

It did not escape the keen observation of the Frenchwoman. "So," she murmured, as she glanced back at the American, "I am a governess

– a dependent – unworthy of your notice. Mr. Horton, the day may come when you will find me no weak enemy!"

She broke into the merry chorus of a gay French song, as she finished speaking, and tripped away, warbling like some joyous bird. None could have dreamed the dark thoughts that lurked beneath that joyous exterior.

Augustus Horton entered the boudoir, and lifting a rose-coloured silken curtain which shrouded the doorway, gazed in silence upon the occupant of the chamber.

The heiress was seated near the open window, her rounded elbow, firm and polished as unveined marble, resting on the cushion of her chair, her head leaning on her hand, her lustrous eyes veiled by the silken lashes that curtained them; her whole attitude bespeaking the profoundest melancholy.

The planter gazed upon her with admiration, but it was admiration unmingled with love.

It was with the same feeling he would have experienced in looking at some gorgeous picture. His *eye* was bewitched by the exquisite colouring, the perfect form; but his *heart* was untouched.

Nothing could be more complete than the contrast between the Spanish girl and the Octoroon.

Both were beautiful – both had eyes of deepest black, but the orbs of Cora Leslie were soft and pensive, while those of Camillia Moraquitos flashed with the burning flames of a southern clime. Cora's oval cheeks were pale as the unsullied leaf of the water-lily; Camillia's glowed with a rich crimson blush, of that splendid hue, rarely seen save in the petals of the damask rose.

But each had offended the pride of the planter, and he determined that each should pay a bitter penalty for having dared to prefer another.

He told his suit and was rejected with scorn. Nay, more, he saw that not only was he utterly indifferent to the Spanish girl – there was something beyond indifference in her manner – something even more powerful than scorn – there was hatred!

Infuriated by this discovery, he determined to fathom her reason. "Camillia Moraquitos," he said, with outward calmness, beneath which raged suppressed passion, "you have rejected the offer of a devoted heart. Be it so! I cannot force your compliance. You love another; no doubt some *honourable* man, whose unsullied name will shed a luster upon the woman he weds."

The Spanish girl's head dropped as Augustus said this, with chilling irony. She felt that he knew her secret, and the bitterness of the sneer wounded her to the heart.

"But this is not all," continued the planter; "not only do you love another, but you *hate* me. I ask you why this is so?"

"Shall I tell you?" she asked gravely, lifting her flashing eyes, and looking him full in the face.

"Yes."

"Heaven forgive me if I wrong you, Augustus Horton, but some secret instinct tells me that you were associated with that pitiful wretch, Silas Craig, in the plot which brought disgrace upon the name of one—"

"Who is very dear to you! Is it not so, Donna Camillia?"

"Yes," she answered, proudly, "I have never before confessed my love to a mortal. I confess it now to you. It will at least prove my belief in his innocence."

"Mr. Paul Lisimon is a very happy man to possess so fair a defender," said Augustus, with studied sarcasm; "no doubt the escaped felon, the runaway thief, will return to New Orleans ere long to claim his bride; though, I fear that the very first hour that he shows his face in this city, he will find himself handcuffed and carried back to gaol. In the mean time, I withdraw all pretensions to your hand. I cannot hope for success against such a rival."

He bowed haughtily, and withdrew, laughing bitterly. In the ante-room without, he found the negro, Tristan, lying on an embroidered rug, close against the boudoir door.

"Dog!" exclaimed Augustus, "you have been listening?"

"Do not be angry, massa, with the poor nigger. What if the dog can help you?"

"Help me?"

"Yes, dogs are sometimes useful. Have you ever seen a bloodhound hunt down a runaway slave, eh, massa? Ah! you have seen that. Many a time, I daresay. Many a time have set the dogs on yourself, to capture your lost property. There are *human bloodhounds*, massa, who can hunt down an enemy as the dog hunts the poor slave. Your enemy is Tristan's enemy too. Say, massa, shall we work together?"

The planter looked at the negro with a glance of contempt.

"What can we have in common?" he said, scornfully.

"Love, massa, love and hate! We both love the same woman, we both hate the same man."

Augustus laughed aloud, "You – you love Camillia Moraquitos?" he exclaimed, with consummate disdain.

"And why not?" cried the negro, striking himself upon the breast; "the heart within is of the same form, though the skin is of another colour. I love her, love her, not as you white men love – but with the passionate fury of the African, which is stronger than death or fate. A jealous fever, which is close akin to hate and murder. I love her, and I know that she would look with loathing on this black face. I know that she can never be mine – but she shall not be *his*. No, no! I could better bear to see her wedded to you, for she would not *love* you. She would pine and die, and I would kill myself upon her grave, and know that she never blest the man she loved. Say, massa, shall I help you?"

Augustus Horton gazed at the negro for some moments, with a look of mingled surprise and disdain. There was something almost terrific in the fiery energy of the African. Something, which in its terror approached almost to sublimity.

"Shall I serve you, massa?" said Tristan.

"Yes," exclaimed the planter, "you shall be my bloodhound, and help me to hunt down my enemies."

120

CHAPTER XX.
HEAVEN HELPS THOSE WHO TRUST IN PROVIDENCE.

FINDING THE GOLD

In the far depths of a Californian forest, the timber roof of a solitary log hut peeped through the trees. It was a dreary dilapidated building, which had been deserted by former settlers, and neglected by those who now dwelt in it. The rough wooden shutters that sheltered the one solitary window were rotting upon their hinges; the wind whistled in shrill cadences through the crevices of the logs.

As far as the eye could reach there was no vestige of any human habitation, while the rustling of the leaves and the hungry howls of the wolves only broke the silence of the night.

It was difficult to imagine this place to be the dwelling of any civilized being; but yet it was tenanted by two men, who had lived in it for the best part of a year, attended by a negro slave, an honest fellow, who served them as faithfully in that dreary retreat as if they had dwelt in a palace.

The night has fallen; the wind shrieks, like some troubled spirit, amid the branches of the trees; red streaks of light gleam through the cracks of the window shutters and the crevices of the rude timber edifice; the door of the hut is securely closed, though in that lonely region there is little need of bolt or bar.

Let us peep into the neglected building, and gaze unseen upon its occupants. The two men are seated on either side of a blazing fire of brushwood and broken timber, while the negro sits on a low stool, at a respectful distance, waiting till his masters may have need of his services.

His honest face beams with good temper and contentment, even in that dreary abode.

But it is not so with his masters. They are both smoking long cherry-stemmed meerschaum pipes, and they sit in silence, their eyes gloomily fixed upon the blazing fire. It is impossible to judge of their rank in life, for they are both dressed in cutaway velveteen coats, corduroy breeches, and great hob-nail boots – serviceable garments suited to their rude life, but which elsewhere would be worn only by labouring men.

They are both in the prime of life, and one is rather handsome; but they have allowed their hair and whiskers to grow in the roughest fashion, and their faces are bronzed by constant exposure to every variety of weather.

The elder of the two is the first to speak.

"Well, Brown," he says, with a sigh of weariness, "nearly a year gone since we set foot in this dreary district and no good done yet."

The younger man shrugged his shoulders as he removed his pipe from his mouth and knocked out the ashes of tobacco upon the rough stone hearth.

"Yes, a year, a year," he muttered, "and no hope of return yet. No hope of justice being done to the innocent, and punishment and confusion brought upon the guilty."

"Brown," said his companion, "do you remember our first meeting?"

"Yes, we met in the streets of San Francisco; both penniless, yet both determined to conquer fortune, and to wring from the bowels of our mother earth the gold which should enable us to achieve the purposes of our lives."

"You remember we formed a chance acquaintance, which afterwards ripened into friendship."

"It did," answered the other man. "But at the same time we entered into a singular agreement. We resolved that whatever our past history might be, it should remain buried in oblivion, so long as we dwelt together in the wilds of California. We agreed that neither should tell his companion the secrets of his life, or the purpose which he had to accomplish in the future; that even our names should be unknown to each other, and that though living together upon the footing of friends and brothers, we should address each other merely as Brown and Smith."

"Yes, this was our bond."

"We further resolved that we would spend the last dollars we possessed in the purchase of a set of implements, and that we would penetrate into the loneliest tract in the continent, into recesses never visited by the herd of gold diggers, whose labours exhaust the soil in districts where the precious ore has been found. We determined to search for our prize where none had sought before us, and we resolved to brave every hardship, to endure every peril, for the several ends of our lives."

"We did."

"At San Francisco we picked up our faithful Sambo yonder," said the man known as Brown, looking to the negro, "and we bought him a bargain."

"Because poor Sambo was lame, massa. Very few gentlemen will buy lame niggers."

"Lame or not, we found you a treasure, Sambo, and between us we soon contrived to cure your lame leg, and made you as sound as the best of us."

"Yes," cried the negro, grinning from ear to ear, "you did, massa, you did. Kind good massa, Sambo never forget."

"Well, Smith, after eight good months' labour in this district we find ourselves—"

"About as well off as when we came here," answered the other; "we contrived to find a little gold dust during our first month's work, and that has enabled us to pay for the supplies we've had from the nearest village, and to keep up the war all the time; but beyond that we've had no luck whatever."

"None; therefore my proposal is that we leave this place to-morrow at daybreak, and try a fresh district?"

The eyes of the man who called himself Smith sparkled at this proposition, but the negro interposed with an exclamation of terror,—

"You'll nebber go to-morrow, massa," he cried; "'scuse poor nigger what ought to mind his own business, but surely massa will nebber go to-morrow!"

"And why not to-morrow?" asked Brown.

"Because to-morrow Friday; massa, Friday bery unlucky day."

"An unlucky day, Sambo, is it?" answered his master; "faith, I think every day has been precious unlucky to us for the last eight months."

The negro shook his woolly head, and showed two rows of white teeth.

"Friday bery unlucky day, massa," he said.

"But," answered Brown, laughing, "if it's an unlucky day for leaving this place, I suppose it's just as unlucky for staying and doing another turn at the pickaxe."

"Don't know that, massa," said the negro, "but Friday bery unlucky day."

"I'll tell you what, then," continued Brown, "suppose we take Sambo's advice for once in a way, Smith, and put off moving to new quarters till the day after to-morrow. We can spend to-morrow in digging the ground about that little creek three miles to the east of this. You remember our passing the spot once on our way home after a hard day's work."

"Perfectly! a miserable, unlikely-looking place enough; I don't fancy if we dug for a twelvemonth we should ever get any good out of it. However, we've wasted so many days that we can't grudge one more, so I'm quite agreeable to stop."

"So be it, then," answered Brown. "Sambo, get our tools in order before you go to bed, and be sure you call us early to-morrow morning."

The two friends flung themselves down upon a couple of rough straw mattresses, and the negro brought out a heap of dried grass and withered leaves which served him as a bed, and upon which he laid himself down after carefully preparing the tools for the morning's work. The two diggers, before they lay down, offered up a short but heartfelt prayer, that Heaven would be pleased to smile upon their honest endeavours and bless their labours.

During the eight months in which they had dwelt in that dreary region they had never once failed to make this supplication, and, fruitless as their toil had been hitherto, their faith had never failed them. They still trusted that a divine and gracious Providence would, in due time, reward their efforts. At daybreak the next morning the three men set out, and walked to the creek at which they were to work before they ate their rough breakfast.

Then, after offering up another prayer, they took their spades and pickaxes and went to work with good will.

But the day wore on and no result attended their labours. The negro, Sambo, worked untiringly, and cheered his masters' toil by his merry songs and grotesque capers.

It grew towards evening, and Brown proposed that they should collect their tools and walk homewards, but Smith was anxious to work for half an hour longer, and his companion was too good-natured to oppose his fancy.

The half hour had nearly expired, the dusk was rapidly gathering round them, the lower branches of the trees were streaked with crimson and gold by the last rays of the setting sun, and Brown was thinking sadly how many a day such as this they had wasted, and how many a sun had gone down upon their disappointment, when he was aroused from his reverie by a loud exclamation from Smith, and a wild shout of joy from the negro.

His companion's spade had struck against a nugget of gold. He had dug the precious lump of ore from its watery bed, and he had fallen upon his knees in the clay and dirt to offer up a thanksgiving to that Eternal Being who alone can give or withhold all blessings.

The man called Brown clasped his hands and lifted his eyes to Heaven, "Oh, merciful Providence!" he cried, "we have waited Thy good pleasure patiently, hopefully, for we knew Thy unfailing justice. It has pleased Thee to smile upon us, and the innocent may now be restored to the happiness of which guilt and chicanery has deprived them."

The three men worked till the moon rose high above their heads. They had struck upon a vein of gold, and their labours were amply rewarded. They returned home laden with the dull yellow metal, which is the master key of all earthly power, the magic influence which can make all men slaves.

They returned the next day to the same spot, and worked again, and continued to do so till they were rich beyond their wildest hopes. Then they packed their wealth in such a manner as to escape suspicion from any unscrupulous travellers they might encounter, and still followed by their faithful slave, Sambo, set out for San Francisco.

"When we once more set foot in the United States," said Brown, as they turned their backs on the dilapidated log hut, "I will tell you my past history, the secret of my life, and the purpose I have to achieve in the future. In the meantime let us remain as we have been before, ignorant of all concerning each other, save that we are both honest men who trust in Providence. Shall it be so?"

"Yes," answered Smith; "friend, brother, it shall be as you say. Heaven shield those we go to save."

"And Heaven help those we go to punish."

"I say, Massa, Massa Smith, Massa Brown, Nigger Sambo is a big old fool; nebber say Friday bery unlucky day again."

CHAPTER XXI.
THE ABDUCTION.

Let us return to New Orleans and to the Villa Moraquitos. An hour after Augustus Horton left the boudoir of Camillia, the Spanish heiress and her companion Pauline Corsi were seated, side by side, in a deep recess of a window, looking out upon the shining waters of the Mississippi.

"So you have rejected him, Camillia?" said Pauline.

"Rejected him!" repeated the Spanish girl, contemptuously, "could you ever dream that I should do otherwise?"

"And yet Augustus Horton is rich, young, handsome, distinguished—"

"He may be all that," interrupted Camillia. "Yet I have no feelings for him but indifference – nay, contempt."

"Shall I tell you the secret of that indifference?" said Pauline, with a smile.

"If you please," answered Camillia, carelessly.

"The secret is your love for another. Ay, that start and blush would betray you had naught else already done so. My foolish Camillia, did you think to conceal the truth from one who had known you from childhood? On the day of Paul Lisimon's apprehension I told him that I had long known all."

"Forgive me, dear Pauline, if I have seemed wanting in candour," said Camillia; "but it was Paul who bade me be silent."

"Yes, Paul, who feared that the governess might betray her pupil. Now, listen to me, Camillia. The story of my life is a strange one. The day may come when I may choose to reveal it, but that day has not arrived. The history of the past may have done much to embitter a heart that was not once all base. I am ambitious – proud – though policy has taught me to conceal my pride – dependence, even on those I like, is painful to me; all this I have learnt to hide beneath a gay exterior."

"Pauline, you terrify me!" exclaimed Camillia, "this power of concealing your feelings—"

"Is akin to falsehood, is it not, Camillia? No matter. For the first time I speak the truth to you about myself. You have been kind, generous, affectionate. I should be worse than a murderess could I break your heart, for to break your heart would be to kill you – and yet, Camillia, three days ago I should have been capable of that infamy."

"Pauline – Pauline!"

"Ah, well may you open those large black eyes with that gaze of horror and amazement. Yes, I repeat, three days ago I should have been capable of this; because I am ambitious, and the ambitious will trample on the most sacred ties to attain the golden goal of their wishes. But this is past. Another road has opened to me, and henceforth, Camillia Moraquitos, I will be your friend. Say, will you trust me?"

Pauline Corsi fixed her large, limped blue eyes upon the face of her pupil, with an earnest glance of inquiry.

"Will you trust me, Camillia?"

"Yes, Pauline! your words have terrified and bewildered me, but I feel that, whatever you may be, you are not deceiving me now."

"I am not, indeed!" answered Pauline; "It is agreed then – you will trust me?"

"I will!"

"Tell me, then, do you love Paul Lisimon?"

"Truly, eternally!"

"And for that love you are prepared to sacrifice all ambitious hopes? – You, who have much of your father's haughty nature, can reconcile yourself to a life of comparative poverty and obscurity for the sake of him you love?"

"It would be no sacrifice," answered Camilla; "poverty would have no trials if shared with him."

"But, remember, Camillia Moraquitos: think of his unknown birth – low and obscure no doubt as are all mysterious lineages – would not that cause you to blush for your lover – your husband?"

"I could never blush for him while I knew him to be honest and honourable."

"Ay, but even then how bitter would be your trial? Do not forget that his honour has been sullied by a foul suspicion – that he has been branded as a thief!"

"I forget nothing. I know that I love him and trust him. We cannot love those we do not trust."

"Enough," answered Pauline, "now listen to me. I tell you that a new road has opened to my ambitious hopes. I shall win wealth and station, without sacrificing you or your lover. Nay, more, I promise you that the day that sees the fulfilment of my wishes, shall also see you the bride of Paul Lisimon."

"Pauline, what do you mean?"

"Seek to know nothing – only trust me. There are dark obscurities in the pathway of guilt, which I would not have you penetrate. I have promised to befriend you in all things. What if the foul plot, which, as I believe, has been hatched by that villainous attorney, Silas Craig, were brought to light by my agency? Would you thank me for that, Camillia?"

"Thank you, Pauline. Oh, if you could but clear him I love from the vile accusations brought against him, I would be your grateful slave to the end of life."

"I do not ask that – I only ask patience and confidence. I hold a power over Silas Craig, which none other possesses, and on the day which crowns my hopes, he shall be made to confess his infamy, and withdraw the charge against Paul Lisimon."

"Pauline, Pauline," exclaimed Camillia; "my benefactress, my preserver."

"Hush!" said the Frenchwoman, laying her finger on her lips, "remember, patience and caution."

As she spoke, Pepita, Camillia's old nurse, entered the room. "Oh, missy," said the faithful mulattress, "there is a sailorman below, who has fine silks and laces to show you, if you'll only look at his merchandise. Such bargains, he says, missy."

"But I don't want to see them," replied Camillia, indifferently; "tell the man to take his goods somewhere else, Pepita."

"Stay," interrupted Pauline; "we may as well look at these bargains."

"Ay, do, Ma'moselle," said Pepita; "it will amuse poor missy. Poor missy very ill lately."

"Why do you wish to see this man?" asked Camillia, when the mulattress had left the apartment.

"Because I have an idea that we should do wrong in refusing to admit him. We shall see whether I am right or not."

Pepita ushered the sailor into her mistress's presence. He was a black-eyed, dark-haired fellow, with a complexion that had grown copper coloured by exposure to the wind and sun. He opened a bale of silks and spread its contents at the feet of the Spanish girl.

Camillia glanced at them with listless indifference.

"They are handsome," she said; "but I have no occasion for them."

"But you will not refuse to buy something of a poor sailor, kind lady?" said the man, in an insinuating tone; "even if you do not wish for a silk dress, there may be something else among my stores that may tempt you to bid for it; see here!" he added, feeling in one of the pockets of his loose trousers, "I've something here that perhaps you may take a fancy to."

He produced a red morocco case, large enough to contain a chain or bracelet.

"Look here," he said, opening it, and holding it towards Camillia, so that she alone could see its contents. "You won't refuse me a dollar or two for that, eh, lady?"

Camillia could not repress a start of surprise. The case contained an imitation gold chain of the commonest workmanship, coiled round in a circle, in the centre of which was a note folded into the smallest possible compass. Upon the uppermost side of this note was written the word "Fidelity," in a handwriting which was well known to the Spanish girl.

"Will you buy the chain, lady?" asked the sailor.

Camillia opened an ormolu casket on a table near her, and took out a handful of dollars, which she dropped into the ample palm of the sailor.

"Will that requite you for your trouble, my good friend?" she asked.

"Right nobly, lady."

"If you can come again to-morrow, I may purchase something more of you."

The sailor grinned; "I'll come if I can, my lady," he answered, and with a rough salute he left the room, followed by Pepita.

"Was I right, Camillia?" asked Mademoiselle Corsi.

"You were, dear Pauline; see, a note in Paul's hand!"

"Shall I leave you to devour its contents?"

"No, Pauline, I have no secrets from you henceforth," answered Camillia, unfolding the precious scrap of paper.

It contained these words:

"Fear not, dearest, and do not think it is guilt which has prompted my flight. Be faithful, and trust me that all will yet be well; and remember that I may be near you when least you look for me. Affect an utter indifference to my fate, and mingle in the gay world as you have ever done. This is necessary to disarm suspicion. Above all, throw Augustus Horton off the scent, and let him believe that I have left America forever.

"Ever and ever yours,

"Paul."

Camillia Moraquitos obeyed the instructions contained in this brief epistle; and when Don Juan entered her boudoir half an hour afterwards, he found his daughter apparently in her usual spirits.

Delighted at this change, he proposed that Camillia and Pauline should go to the opera that evening, attended by himself, and the ladies assented with every semblance of gratitude. The Opera House was thronged that night with all the rank and fashion of New Orleans. It was the occasion of the re-appearance of a brilliant Parisian actress and singer who had lately returned to Louisiana after a twelve months absence in France.

The box occupied by Don Juan was one of the best in the house, and amongst all assembled, there was none lovelier or more admired than Camillia Moraquitos.

The Spanish girl wore a dress of rich amber silk, flounced with the costliest black lace. Her classically moulded head was encircled by a simple band of gold, studded with diamonds. She waved a perfumed fan of ebony and gold in her small gloved hand.

They had not been long seated in the box when they were joined by Augustus Horton, who placed himself at the back of the chair occupied by Camillia.

She was not a little surprised at this, after the interview of that morning, and the terrible and insulting repulse which the young planter had received.

While she was wondering what could have induced him to forget this, he bent his head and whispered in her ear—

"Let us forget all that passed this morning, Donna Camillia," he said; "forget and forgive my presumption as I forgive your cruelty! Let us be what we were before to-day, friends, and friends only."

Camillia raised her eyes to his face with a glance of surprise. Was this the man whose words that morning had breathed rage and vengeance? Had she wronged him in imagining him vindictive and treacherous?

Don Juan knew nothing of his daughter's rejection of Augustus Horton. He imagined, therefore, from the planter's presence in the box, that his suit had prospered.

About half an hour after the rising of the curtain, a letter was brought by one of the boxkeepers addressed to Don Juan Moraquitos.

"Who gave you this?" asked the Spaniard.

"A coloured lad, sir, who said he was to wait for an answer," replied the boxkeeper.

"Tell him that I will see to it."

The man left the box and Don Juan opened the letter.

It was from Silas Craig, and contained only a couple of lines, requesting to see his employer without delay, on business of importance.

Don Juan rose to leave the box.

"I am never permitted to enjoy the society of my only daughter for a few hours without interruption," he said, bending gently over Camillia. "I am summoned away on some annoying business, but I will not be gone long, darling."

"But how long, dearest father?"

"An hour at most. Meanwhile I leave you in the care of Mr. Horton."

"I accept the trust," answered Augustus, with enthusiasm.

In spite of the letter she had that morning received, Camillia found it impossible to simulate a gaiety which she did not feel. She was silent and absent-minded, and replied in monosyllables to the gallant speeches of her admirer. She was thinking of the events of the day – Pauline Corsi's promise and the letter from Paul Lisimon.

Once in looking downwards at the crowd of faces in the pit of the theatre, she recognized one which was turned to the box in which she was seated, instead of to the stage. It was the copper coloured visage of the sailor who had that morning brought her Paul's letter.

She knew not why, but she felt a thrill of pleasurable emotion vibrating through her breast as she beheld the rough face of this man. He knew, and was known to Paul. He could not then be other than a friend to her.

The watchful eye of Augustus Horton perceived her start of surprise as she beheld this man.

"One would think," he said, with something of a sneer, "that the lovely Donna Camillia Moraquitos had recognized an acquaintance in the pit of the theatre."

Camillia did not reply to this remark. It was growing late and Don Juan had not returned. His daughter was unable to repress a feeling of uneasiness at his lengthened absence. The Spaniard's affection for his only child was the one strong passion of his heart. No lover could have been more attentive than he to his daughter's slightest wish.

"Strange," murmured Camillia, as the after-piece drew to a close; "my father never fails to keep his word, yet it is now three hours since he left us."

The curtain fell, and the audience rose to leave the house.

"I will go and look for your carriage, Donna Camillia," said Augustus; "perhaps I may find your father waiting for you in the corridor without."

He left the box and returned in about three minutes to say that the carriage was at the door. Camillia's anxious eye detected something of agitation in his manner.

"My father," she said; "did you see him?"

"No, no," he answered, in rather a confused manner, offering his arm to Camillia, "I have not seen him yet. But pray let me lead you to your carriage, the corridors and lobbies are terribly crowded."

He took no notice whatever of Pauline Corsi, who followed as she best could, but who was speedily separated from them by the crowd, and by the rapidity with which Augustus hurried Camillia through the passages and down the staircase.

By the time they had reached the portico of the theatre, they had completely lost sight of the French governess. Augustus handed the Spanish girl so quickly into a carriage that she was not able to take any particular notice of the vehicle; but when seated inside, she saw, from the gleam of the lamps without, that the cushions and linings were of a different colour to those of her own equipage.

"Mr. Horton," she exclaimed, "this is not my carriage." Augustus was standing at the door as she spoke.

"No matter!" he said; "we have no time to lose; drive on," he added, addressing the negro on the box, and at the same moment he sprang into the carriage and drew up the window.

Camillia was bewildered and alarmed by his conduct.

"You have forgotten Pauline," she exclaimed; "we are leaving her behind us."

"Mademoiselle Corsi must shift for herself," answered the planter, as the carriage drove rapidly away, and turning out of the brilliantly lighted thoroughfare, plunged into one of the darkest streets in New Orleans. "I have wished to spare you all anxiety, Donna Camillia, but concealment can no longer avail. Your father has been taken ill, and has sent for you."

"My father ill! dangerously ill?"

"I do not say that."

"But perhaps it is so. Oh, Heaven, my beloved and honoured father – that noble and generous friend who never denied a wish of my heart – tell them to drive faster, for pity's sake! Let us lose no time in reaching him!"

She turned to Augustus Horton with clasped hands raised in supplication. At the very moment when she thus appealed to him, the carriage passed a corner of a street at which there was a lamp.

The light of this lamp flashed upon the face of the planter as they drove rapidly by. Brief as the moment was, Camillia fancied she detected a smile of triumph upon the countenance of Augustus Horton.

A thrill of horror crept through her veins as she thought that perhaps this alarm about her father was some vile subterfuge of her rejected lover.

She had often heard – heard with a careless and unheeding ear, of deeds of darkness done in the city of her birth. She knew that the wealthy members of New Orleans society were not over scrupulous in the gratification of their viler passions – and she trembled as she thought of her helplessness – but she had the brave spirit of her father's race, and she had sufficient presence of mind to conceal her terror.

She determined upon testing her companion.

"Why did not my father send his own carriage for me?" she asked.

"Because Don Juan was not taken ill at the Villa Moraquitos. He was attacked in a gaming-house at the other end of the city, and it is thither I'm taking you."

"My father stricken with illness in a gaming-house!" said Camillia. "My father a gambler?"

"Ay, that surprises you no doubt. There are many secrets in this city of ours, Donna Camillia, and your father knows how to keep his. It was to avoid all scandal that I brought you away from the Opera House by a species of stratagem. It would not have done for that brilliant assembly to know whither I was bringing you."

"It is to some infamous haunt then?" said Camillia.

"All vices are infamous," answered the planter. "It is to the haunt of the rich and idle – the aristocratic and dissipated. But perhaps your womanly nature shrinks from this ordeal. If it be so, I will drive you home without delay. There is no absolute necessity for your seeing your father to-night. To-morrow he may be well enough to return to the Villa Moraquitos, and in the meantime I do not think there is any serious danger."

These last words were uttered slowly and hesitatingly, as if the speaker felt them to be untrue, and only spoke them in the desire to comfort his companion.

Camillia's suspicions were completely dispelled.

"You do not *think* he is in danger?" she exclaimed. "Can you imagine Camillia Moraquitos so poor a coward as to shrink from visiting her beloved father because he lies in a gambling-house? Had he been stricken in the most infamous den in New Orleans, I would enter it alone to comfort and succour him."

Had there been a lamp near to illumine the planter's face at this moment, Camillia might have again beheld the triumphant smile which had before alarmed her.

Five minutes after this the carriage stopped at a low door, in a dark but highly respectable-looking street. The negro coachman kept his seat, but Augustus sprang on to the pavement and handed Camillia out of the vehicle.

The door before which they had stopped appeared to be closed so securely as to defy all the burglars in New Orleans.

Yet Augustus Horton neither knocked nor rang for admission; there was a brass-plate upon the door; he simply pressed his finger against one of the letters engraved upon this plate, and the door opened slowly and noiselessly.

The passage within was unillumined by one ray of light. "Give me your hand, Donna Camillia," whispered the planter. The brave-hearted girl obeyed, and Augustus led her cautiously onwards.

As he did so she heard the door close behind her with a muffled sound.

They ascended a narrow winding staircase, at the top of which they entered a long corridor, lighted by shaded gas-lamps, which emitted a subdued radiance.

At the end of the corridor Augustus Horton opened the door of a room, into which he led Camillia. In this room she expected to find her father; but she was cruelly disappointed. The apartment was handsomely furnished, and lighted with a lamp which hung from the ceiling, and which, like those in the corridor, shed a subdued and shadowy light; but it was empty.

Camillia looked hurriedly around her. All her suspicions had returned at the aspect of the place to which the planter had brought her. The door opening by its mysterious spring, the dark passage and winding stair, the strange silence of the place in which their footsteps sounded as if they had been shod with felt – all combined to inspire terror.

"My father! my father!" she exclaimed. "Where is he?"

"Heaven knows," answered Augustus, "perhaps searching for you in the portico of the Opera House. Camillia Moraquitos, you are young and new to a world in which men have passionate and revengeful hearts. You have much to learn, but you will take a lesson, it may be, ere long. This morning you insulted me; *to-night you are in my power!*"

CHAPTER XXII.
THE ENCOUNTER IN THE GAMBLING HOUSE.

As the planter uttered the horrible threat, contained in our last chapter, every drop of blood fled from the cheeks and lips of Camillia Moraquitos, leaving them pale and colder than marble.

"This morning you insulted me – *to-night you are in my power!*"

It was then as she expected – as she had feared. She was entrapped – cajoled – in the power of a villain and a hypocrite.

She knew not even in what quarter of the city this mysterious house was situated.

She was utterly ignorant of its character or its occupants.

It might be the den of a band of thieves – the haunt of a gang of murderers – and she was alone, alone with a man who evidently hated her with the vengeful hate of a wicked and vindictive soul.

Yet even in this terrible emergency, her courage did not forsake her. Her high and noble spirit rebounded after the shock which had, for one brief moment, depressed it. She looked at Augustus Horton, gazing upon him with such a glance of mingled horror and loathing, that the meanest hound would have shrunk from the contemptuous expression of her superb countenance.

"I thought you a villain," she said, with cold deliberation, unmixed with terror; "but I did not think you were capable of such a deed as this. There were depths of black infamy which I had yet to fathom. I thank you for teaching me their black extent."

"You shall thank me for a better lesson before we part, Camillia Moraquitos."

Again the Spanish girl looked at him with the same cold and withering gaze.

"I do not fear you," she murmured between her clinched teeth; "I can suffer – but I can also die!"

Her small white hand wandered almost mechanically to the bosom of her silken dress, where, concealed by the rich folds of black lace, lurked the jewelled hilt of a small dagger.

It was a glittering toy, a bauble which, after the custom of her Spanish ancestry, she wore sometimes when the whim seized her – but, plaything though it was, the blade was of the finest Toledo steel and workmanship.

"I can die," she repeated, as her fingers entwined themselves convulsively about the gemmed hilt of this tiny weapon.

"Ay, lady," answered Augustus, with the bitter irony of some triumphant fiend, "you can die here, stabbed to the heart by your own hand, that jewelled dagger buried in your breast. And when your corpse is found here to-morrow, by the astounded police, what think you will be said by the scandalmongers of New Orleans? If you knew them, Donna Camillia, as well as I, you would be able to guess what they will say. They will whisper to each other how the lovely and haughty daughter of Don Juan Moraquitos went to meet her lover at midnight, in one of the secret chambers of a certain gambling-house; where, on being pursued thither by her infuriated father, the unhappy girl, overcome by despair, drew a dagger from her bosom and stabbed herself to the heart. This is what will be said, unless I am much deceived in human nature."

"Oh, misery!" exclaimed Camillia.

"And even should the worthy citizens of New Orleans fail to put this interpretation upon your death, a few judicious whispers dropped by my chosen friends – a smile of triumph, and a shrug of the shoulders from myself will soon set afloat any report I please. So think twice before you use that pretty plaything, Donna Camillia," added the planter, pointing to the hilt she grasped in her hand; "think twice if you are prudent, and remember that death to-night, and in this house, is not death alone – *it is disgrace!*"

The young girl buried her face in her hands. She shuddered, but she did not speak.

Augustus Horton perceived that involuntary shudder, and an exclamation of triumph escaped his lips.

"Ah, proud Spanish woman, you whom the wealthiest and most aristocratic Creole of New Orleans is not worthy to wed, you no longer defy me then. You tremble though those stubborn lips refuse to entreat – those haughty knees cannot stoop to kneel – you tremble! Now listen to me!"

He pushed a chair towards her. She sank into it and, as if with an effort, removed her hands from her face. Whatever struggle she had endured in these few brief moments, she had conquered herself once more, and her face, though pale as death, was calm as that of a statue.

"Listen to me, Camillia Moraquitos," repeated the planter, resting his hand upon the back of her chair and addressing her with deliberate and icy distinctness. "I sought to wed you for your beauty, your aristocratic bearing, and your wealth. You, amidst all the beauties of Louisiana, were the only woman whom I should have wished to place at the head of my table – to make the mistress of my house. Your beauty would have been mine – a part of my possessions; my pride, my boast. It would have pleased me to see you haughty and capricious – treading the earth as if the soil were scarcely good enough to be trodden by your Andalusian foot. Your wealth would have swelled my own large fortune, and made me the richest man in New Orleans. This, then, is why I sought to wed you. This is why I seek to wed you still."

"And more vainly now than ever," murmured Camillia.

"Not so fast, lady; we will test your resolution by and bye. I have told you why I wooed you, but I have something yet more to tell you."

"I am listening, sir."

"I never loved you! No, beautiful as you are, I can gaze with rapture upon your gorgeous face, but it is the rapture of an artist who beholds a priceless picture in some Italian gallery. I admire, and that is all. No throb of warmer emotion disturbs the even beating of my heart. I love – but, like yourself, who have stooped to bestow your affection upon the obscure and penniless dependent of your father – I love one below me in station – below me so infinitely that even were I so weak a fool as to wish it, the laws of New Orleans would not permit me to make her my wife. I love a daughter of the accursed race – a slave – an Octoroon."

"What motive, then, could you have in bringing me hither?" said Camillia.

"*What* motive!" exclaimed the planter; "a motive far stronger than love – that motive is revenge. You have insulted me, Donna Camillia, and you have to learn that none ever yet dared to insult Augustus Horton with impunity. I threaten no terrible punishment," he added, looking at his watch; "it is now two o'clock; when the morning sun rises upon New Orleans, and the streets begin to fill with traffic, I will reconduct you to the Villa Moraquitos. You will suffer from this night's business in no other way save one, and that is your reputation, which you can only repair by accepting your humble servant as a husband."

"Coward, dastard, do you think I will ever consent to this?"

"I think on reflection you will see the prudence of doing so."

For a few moments Camillia remained silent, then, turning upon the planter with a sudden energy that threw him completely off his guard, she exclaimed:–

"Augustus Horton, you talk to me of prudence. Shall I tell you what you will do if you are wise."

"Yes, Donna Camillia. I am all attention."

"You will kill me here upon this spot. You will conceal my corpse in one of the secret recesses with which this den of infamy no doubt abounds. If you have one spark of prudence you will do this, for I swear to you by the stars of heaven that if I ever leave this place alive I shall pay dearly for your conduct of to-night."

"You threaten me, Donna Camillia – here!"

"Ay, here, though this house were tenanted with murderers. Do you think my father, Don Juan Moraquitos, will spare the destroyers of his daughter's unsullied name?"

"Don Juan will believe that which the rest of New Orleans will believe. You will tell your story, but your father, fondly as he may love you, will smile at its incredulity. Your midnight abduction, your being brought hither to a strange house – whose very locality you will be unable to name – your inability to call upon one witness to support your story – all will confirm the scandal; and your father, who, yesterday morning, refused to coerce your wishes, will to-morrow compel you to become my wife."

"Sooner than my father should think me the base and degraded wretch you would make me appear, I will die by my own hand, even though the disgrace of this haunt of crime were to cling to me in death; but I will not die without a struggle. Whoever the tenants of this house may be, there may be one amongst them who yet retains one spark of pity – there may be one who would not hear a woman's voice uplifted in distress without one attempt to succour."

As she spoke she perceived a gathering look of alarm in the face of Augustus Horton. That look determined her.

"Come the worst," she cried, "I will make the appeal!"

"Beware!" he cried. "The people here are not scrupulous."

"I care not!" she answered. "I can but die!"

"But you shall die in silence!" exclaimed the planter, springing towards her, and clutching the hand which grasped the dagger.

He was too late. Her voice rang through the building in a shrill and piercing scream.

In the deathly silence of the night that sound seemed multiplied by a thousand echoes. It vibrated in the furthest corners of the edifice. To the planter's terrified ear it seemed as if the whole city of New Orleans must have been aroused by that one woman's cry.

Desperate and infuriated he snatched the dagger from Camillia's grasp, and placing his hand upon her mouth, was about to bury the weapon in her breast, when the door was broken open by a tremendous blow from without, and three men burst into the room.

These three men were Captain Prendergills, of the schooner Amazon, the sailor who had carried Paul's letter to Camillia, and Paul Lisimon himself.

"So," exclaimed the Captain, "we're right, are we? This is where the noise came from. What do you mean by it, you thundering landlubber? How is it that a gentleman can't take a fling at the dice without being disturbed by a woman's squeal?"

Before Augustus could answer, Paul Lisimon pushed aside the Captain and clasped Camillia in his arms.

"My Camillia," he cried; "my beloved, how is it that I find you here – here, in a gambling-house at this hour of the night?"

"Ask me no questions," muttered the Spanish girl, "only take me from this place. My brain is bewildered by what I have undergone."

"But this man – has he dared to insult you – to entrap you hither?" asked Paul, pointing to Augustus Horton, who stood at bay, while the Captain and the sailor threatened him with their drawn cutlasses.

"He has."

"You hear this fainting girl," exclaimed Paul, still holding Camillia clasped in his left arm, while with his right he felt for a pistol in the bosom of his waistcoat. "Prendergills – Joe! – you are witnesses of the place in which we have found the only daughter of Don Juan Moraquitos! There is some foul plot here, and that man, Augustus Horton, is the mover of it. To-morrow, sir, you shall account to me for this."

The planter laughed mockingly. "Account to *you*, Mr. Paul Lisimon; to *you* – a thief! an escaped felon! The colonists of Louisiana do not cross swords with such as you. You would have done wiser to keep clear of New Orleans. Above all, it would have been better for you had you refrained from crossing my path."

He touched a bell in the wall behind him, and it rang through the house with a shrill peal.

"Now, Mr. Lisimon," he said, "we are quits."

A party of about twenty men crowded into the room. The bell had summoned them from the gaming-table.

"Gentlemen," cried Augustus Horton, "I call upon you as citizens of New Orleans to secure the persons of these three men who have this moment made a murderous attack upon my life, and endeavoured to carry away this lady, who is here under my protection. One of them is an escaped felon from the gaol of this city."

The gamblers, who were almost all in some degree intoxicated, made a rush at Paul and his companions, but they were many of them unarmed, and those who carried knives flourished them without aim or purpose.

"Prendergills – Joe!" exclaimed Lisimon, "follow me. Remember, it is for life or death."

Then flinging the slender form of Camillia across his shoulder, the young Mexican flung himself in the midst of the infuriated crowd, and, pistol in hand, boldly made for the door.

This point gained, he stood upon the threshold with his back to the passage, defending the ground inch by inch, until joined by Prendergills and Joe.

The rest was comparatively easy. The three men fought their way backwards along the passage, down the winding staircase to the street door. Here they were for a moment baffled by the mystery of the spring which closed the entrance. But they were not to be so easily foiled; the Captain of the Amazon flung his gigantic frame against the door, the wooden panels cracked as if they had been made of glass, and the spring was burst asunder. The door – which was used all the night through for the entrance and egress of the gamblers who frequented the house – was only fastened by this spring, and therefore yielded to force more easily than an ordinary barrier. Once in the street, Paul and his friends were safe. The gamblers dared not pursue them another step, for to do so would have been to reveal the secret of the gaming-house, which, as the reader knows, held its ground in defiance of the laws of Louisiana.

Mad with baffled rage and fury, Augustus Horton returned to his own house to await the coming of the morrow, which would perhaps dawn upon a deadly encounter between himself and Don Juan Moraquitos. To his surprise, he received no tidings from the Spaniard, but a little after noon his mulatto valet handed him two letters. One was in the handwriting of Camillia Moraquitos. It breathed the contempt which a noble mind feels for the cowardice of a dastard. It ran thus:–

"As the life of a beloved father is far too valuable to be risked in an encounter with a wretch so degraded as yourself, Don Juan Moraquitos will never be told the true history of the events of last night. Rest therefore in security: beneath contempt, too low for revenge."

The second letter was from Paul Lisimon. It was even briefer than that of Camillia.

"You shall yet answer to me for the outrage committed on one who is dearer to me than life. For to-day you triumph; but a day of reckoning will come ere long. I wait.

     "PAUL LISIMON."

CHAPTER XXIII.
THE FATAL DAY.

THE ATTEMPTED ESCAPE

The bullet wound which had prostrated Gilbert Margrave in the forest at Iberville was a very serious one. For many days and nights he lay in one of the apartments of the Pavilion, near Lake Pont Chartrain, in a state which was not entirely without danger. But he had the best medical attendance which New Orleans could afford, and the tenderest care which affection can secure for the object on which it lavishes its wealth.

Night and day Cora Leslie and the mulatto slave Toby watched beside the pillow of the wounded man. It was they and they alone, who listened to the wandering accents of delirium; they who soothed and comforted in the hour of suffering; they who cheered and animated when the danger was past, and the first faint glimpse of returning health re-illumined the cheek of the invalid.

Gerald Leslie was away from home. When the boat carrying Gilbert Margrave, Cora, Mortimer and Toby reached the Pavilion, the planter had already departed for New York, leaving a few brief lines addressed to his daughter, telling her only that urgent business had called him from the South.

The father and daughter had therefore never met since that hour in which the Octoroon had accused Gerald Leslie of being the cause of her mother's death.

The two months for which the bill, for a hundred thousand dollars due to Silas Craig, had been renewed, were rapidly gliding away, and every day made the position of Gerald Leslie more alarming.

Cora knew nothing of these pecuniary troubles. She thought that her father had deserted his home rather than endure her reproaches, and she bitterly upbraided herself for the cruel words she had spoken to one whose faults were rather those of circumstance than inclination.

Gilbert Margrave recovered; but he still lingered beneath Gerald Leslie's roof; for the planter had written to him from New York, thanking him earnestly for his championship of Cora, and imploring him to remain at Lake Pont Chartrain until his return.

Gilbert waited, therefore, until the presence of Mr. Leslie might enable him to make the necessary arrangements for his marriage with the Octoroon.

He was well aware that he could not marry her in New Orleans; but he knew that in free England there is no barrier to separate an honourable man from the woman of his choice.

It was now upon the very eve of the date upon which the dreaded bill of exchange was to fall due, and at eleven o'clock upon the night preceding the fatal day, Gerald Leslie returned to the Pavilion upon the borders of Lake Pont Chartrain.

Cora had retired to rest when her father arrived; but Gilbert Margrave was walking alone upon the terrace, overlooking the lake upon which the moonbeams shed their soft lustre.

He was, therefore, the first to welcome Mr. Leslie, and he was not long in perceiving that some heavy trouble was weighing upon the mind of Cora's father.

"You must be fatigued after your long journey, Mr. Leslie," said Gilbert. "I feel called upon to play the host beneath your own roof. Pray let us go in. Toby will prepare you some refreshments."

"No, no, Mr. Margrave," answered Gerald; "I want nothing. I am too much excited to require even repose. Let us remain here – here we can converse freely. Toby is a faithful fellow, but he knows too much already of my misfortunes. Where is Cora?"

"She has retired to rest."

"That is well. Poor girl! Poor girl!" He sighed heavily, and relapsed into silence.

The two men walked side by side up and down the terrace for some minutes without uttering a word. Gilbert Margrave was the first to speak.

"Pardon me, Mr. Leslie," he said, "but I fear you have some cause for unhappiness. Remember how dear you and yours are to me, and do not scruple to confide in me, do not hesitate to command my services. They are yours to the death."

"My noble boy, you have already proved that," exclaimed Gerald Leslie. "Gilbert Margrave, I am a ruined man. My journey to New York has been a useless one. I went to endeavour to raise a sum of money which would free me from my embarrassment, but I found trade in a state of convulsion from the threatened war between the North and South, and my mission failed. I have now but one hope. The house of Richardson, of Broadway, have promised, if possible, to advance the sum I require. The money is to arrive by the next steamer. But even this is a forlorn hope, for, when I left New York, dark rumours were afloat of the approaching bankruptcy of that very firm. If this should happen, I am utterly lost. I shall remain to the very last to struggle against evil fortune, but I must remain alone. Tell me then, Mr. Margrave, do you still persist in your proposal for my daughter's hand?"

"Can you doubt it?"

"With a perfect knowledge of her story – remembering that she is the offspring of a slave – that she is an Octoroon!"

"I remember nothing but that I love her, and would have her no other than she is."

"I was not mistaken in you, Gilbert Margrave," replied Mr. Leslie, with suppressed emotion. "You are a man of honour, and it is to that honour I confide. You must fly from New Orleans with Cora. We must not expose her to the violence of a populace, furious against her because of her fatal birth – because she is a slave. That word does not cause you the horror it inspires in me, yet you are no doubt aware that the condition of the child is the same as that of the mother."

"But why not affranchise her?"

"Affranchise her!" exclaimed Gerald Leslie. "Would the law permit me? No, I cannot purchase her freedom until she attains her thirtieth year, unless indeed I could have my motives approved by the magistrate of the parish and three-fourths of a jury. And do you think those motives would be approved at such a time as this, when the public mind is infuriated against all those who would weaken the bonds of slavery? You shudder to behold the love of a father powerless against the laws of this land. It is terrible, is it not?"

"It is infamous," exclaimed Gilbert, "but what is there to be done?"

"You must leave Louisiana. Your marriage can only take place in a free state, for here you cannot make Cora your wife without swearing that you have negro blood in your veins. See the British Consul, obtain from him the means of leaving in safety, and implore him to grant Cora a shelter at his house until you're ready to leave New Orleans. You can conduct her thither at daybreak to-morrow. Closely veiled, she will at that early hour escape observation. To you I confide the task of preparing her for this step. You will have little difficulty in persuading her, for she loves you, and she will leave Louisiana without one pang of regret."

"Nay, Mr. Leslie," said the young man; "you wrong her, believe me—"

Gerald Leslie checked him by a rapid gesture.

"For pity's sake not a word," he murmured. "At some future day, when the bitterness of all this suffering has become a memory of the past; when she is happy, and – has well nigh forgotten me – then recall to her the name of her father; tell her – tell her that I loved her. It will be better for both that we should be spared the pang of parting; so I will see her no more, though it is my very life which I lose in losing her. You will write to me, Gilbert?"

"Yes, yes, dear sir," exclaimed the Englishman, clasping his hand.

"Farewell, then, farewell, Gilbert, my son. You will be kind to her for my sake; you will love her dearly, will you not? Farewell."

He wrung the hand which clasped his, and then breaking from Gilbert Margrave, rushed into the house.

The young engineer slowly followed him, and retiring to his own room, made all preparations for the journey. It was already long past midnight, and Gilbert was too much agitated to require rest. At early dawn his arrangements were complete, and summoning Toby, he gave the faithful mulatto a message to carry to Cora's apartments.

This message was an earnest request that the young girl would meet him in the gardens below without delay.

He had not long to await; he descended to the terrace, and in less than ten minutes he was joined by the Octoroon, who looked pale and anxious in the early morning light.

She scarcely paused for their customary greeting.

"My father arrived last night, Gilbert," she said, "and you and he were together for some time, were you not?"

"We were, Cora."

"Tell me, then, what passed between you?"

"He communicated sad news to me, Cora! A thousand dangers threaten us. He trembles for you, and he commands our immediate departure from Louisiana. It is for that purpose that I summoned you so early. We are to start this very morning."

"Leave Louisiana, and without him?"

"Yes, without him. He is determined to stay until the last, to fight against ruin; but he will not have you share his danger. The carriage will be ready in a few moments – all arrangements are made. I am to take you from here to the house of the British Consul, and thence, please Heaven, to a free state, where I am to make you my wife."

"But why does my father dismiss me thus – without one word of affection or farewell?"

"Nay, Cora," replied Gilbert Margrave, "do not accuse him. His last words were words of love, broken by sobs of anguish."

"And you told him that I should consent to this parting?" asked the Octoroon.

"I did, Cora!"

"Oh, Gilbert, could you think me so base? Was it not to share my father's sufferings that I came from England to Louisiana? and can he think that I should be so pitiful a coward as to forsake him in his hour of peril? No, no; while he remains his daughter will stay by his side; when he flies she will accompany him."

"Cora, Cora – angelic girl! Let it be as you will. I will obey you!" exclaimed the engineer.

"Tell me, Gilbert, why you were to go to your Consul?"

"To smooth the way for our departure, and to confide you to his hospitality."

"Go, then," said Cora; "go, but without me. Engage our berths in an English vessel. We will leave Louisiana; but we will leave with my father. This evening you will let us know the result of your mission."

"But if in the meantime—"

"What can you fear? It is but for a few hours, and this evening we shall meet never to part again. See, here comes Toby to say that the carriage is ready. Farewell, Gilbert, till you return to tell us that all is happily arranged."

"The carriage is ready, massa," said Toby, appearing at the top of the terrace steps.

"Come, Gilbert; I will accompany you to the lower garden," said Cora.

They descended the steps side by side, and traversed the winding pathway, followed by Toby.

At the door of the carriage Gilbert Margrave clasped the Octoroon in his arms, and, pressing her to his heart, exclaimed with emotion, "Farewell, my beloved! Even this brief parting is pain and anguish to me. May Heaven bless and guard you!"

There had been a silent spectator of the interview between Gilbert Margrave and Cora. Gerald Leslie had been standing behind the striped blinds in his apartment, which overlooked the terrace, watching the meeting of his daughter and her lover. He saw them descend the terrace steps, and he thought that Cora had readily consented to depart. He heard the carriage wheels roll away upon the smooth gravel road, and the bitterness of his feelings utterly overcame him. "She is gone!" he exclaimed; "gone, without casting one regretful look upon the home she is leaving. She is glad to fly with this man; she loves him; she is his! Ungrateful girl! But what then, was it not my wish? She is saved at last.

Thank Heaven for that! She is saved, and I am alone! I shall never see my child again."

Overpowered by his grief he sunk into a chair, while his head fell forward on his clasped hands.

He had remained thus for some moments, when the door behind him was gently opened, and a soft footstep stole towards him. He raised his head, and beheld his daughter kneeling at his feet.

She twined her arms about his neck, and he clasped her to his heart with passionate emotion.

"Cora," he exclaimed; "Cora, is it you?"

"Dearest father, how could you think that your daughter would consent to depart without you!"

"Alas, alas, my unhappy child!" murmured Gerald.

"But, my father, why this terror, this agitation? What is it you fear?"

"Nothing, nothing, Cora. Shall not I be here to guard and save you? My Cora, my darling, you love me then, you forgive me?"

"Forgive you? My father, it is I who would ask forgiveness."

Once more the planter strained her to his heart.

"This moment repays me for all I have suffered," he exclaimed. "Oh, Heaven, I am too happy!" Then rising, with a gesture of terror, he cried, "Happy, did I say? Happy, when— hark!"

He paused, clasping Cora in his arms, and listening intently.

The voices of several men were to be heard in the vestibule below, and at the same time hurried footsteps sounded on the stairs. Toby rushed breathless into the room.

"Oh, massa, massa, the dreadful day has come at last! Mr. Craig is below with the sheriffs; he has come to take possession of the estate – of all!"

"Already?" exclaimed Gerald Leslie; "then we are lost."

The agitation of the morning had been too much for the Octoroon; this last shock completely prostrated her, and she sank, fainting, into her father's arms.

"My daughter!" cried Gerald, "my child – Toby, the child you nursed – is there no escape, no way to save her?"

The mulatto wrung his hands in silent anguish; then with a gleam of hope illumining his dusky face, he exclaimed,–

"Stay, massa; the garden below this communicates with the plantation; if we could reach that, they could never find us. They are all below in the vestibule – wait, wait!"

He rushed from the room, leaving Gerald Leslie in utter bewilderment as to what he was about to do; but in three minutes he appeared at the open window of the apartment, standing at the top of a ladder.

"See, massa," he cried, "we will save her yet. Give her into Toby's arms, and he will save her, though his own life pays the price of her liberty."

It was too late. As the faithful mulatto stretched forth his arms to receive the prostrate form of the unconscious girl, a harsh voice in the garden below exclaimed–

"What are you up to there, you nigger? I see you. If you don't come down quicker than a streak of greased lightning, I guess you'll get a bit of lead in your precious carcass that'll bring you down a sight faster than you went up. Come down, you old cuss, will you?"

The speaker was one of the men employed by the sheriff, who had crept round from the vestibule to the gardens to see if there were any doors or windows by which some of the live stock might escape.

The "LIVE STOCK" is the name given to the slaves upon a plantation. Human beings, with hearts capable of grief and affection, fidelity and love – but in the eyes of the auctioneer, mere cattle to be knocked down by his hammer to the highest bidder.

Amongst the *live stock* was counted Cora, the Octoroon, the lovely and accomplished daughter of Gerald Leslie, the destined bride of Gilbert Margrave.

CHAPTER XXIV.
THE SEPARATION.

THE LAW OF SLAVERY

All hope of escape was over. The mulatto slowly descended the ladder, muttering to the man below that he had only been making some alterations in the window shutters. Cora Leslie re-opened her eyes to behold her father bending over her, his face almost ghastly with agitation.

The Octoroon was terrified by the pale and horror-stricken countenance. "Is it all a dream?" she murmured, passing her hand across her forehead; "speak, dearest father, what has happened?"

"I am ruined, Cora," answered Gerald Leslie, in a hoarse whisper. "But come the worst, we love each other. There is no dark cloud between us now. We may be penniless, but at least we are united."

The reader must understand that, as yet, the Octoroon was unaware of all the miseries of her position. Educated in England – reared upon a free soil, where slavery is unknown, she never dreamt that she would be sold because of her father's insolvency. She had neither seen nor heard of a slave sale. How was she to imagine that she, delicately nurtured, tenderly beloved, was to be sold with all the other goods and chattels upon the estate?

"Come the worst, dearest father," she repeated, "we will never part again."

Gerald Leslie was silent. He had no power to speak. Taking his daughter by the hand, he led her down stairs into the largest apartment in the Pavilion, where Silas Craig, with the sheriff and his assistants, were assembled.

The hardest heart might have been melted as the father and daughter entered the room. Cora, pale and trembling, yet lovely in her pallor, robed in white, and graceful as those lilies which seemed the best emblems of her delicate beauty; Gerald Leslie, proud, calm, and erect, although despair was stamped on every feature of his face. But the brutal nature of Silas Craig was incapable of pity; he felt only a fiendish joy in the humiliation of one who had always despised him.

"I expected to see you, Mr. Craig," said Gerald, addressing the lawyer, with icy contempt, "but I thought that you would come alone. May I ask why you are accompanied by these people?"

"Merely as a matter of precaution," answered Silas; "I have no doubt these gentlemen will find their presence useless; for of course you are prepared to meet your engagements. You have not forgotten that this is the day that your acceptance for a hundred thousand dollars falls due. Mr. Horton has given me full power to act in his name as well as my own. Have you the money ready, my dear Mr. Leslie?"

Gerald Leslie felt the sting of the mocking sneer with which these words were accompanied.

"I am not yet prepared with the money," he answered; "but I have every reason to hope the New York steamer will bring the required sum before night."

"It is from the house of Richardson you expect the money, I believe," said Silas Craig.

"It is."

"In that case I am sorry to inform you that a telegram has just reached New Orleans announcing the failure of that house."

Gerald Leslie clasped his hands in silence.

"Was that your only resource, Mr. Leslie?" asked Craig.

Still the planter made no reply.

"You see, then," continued the lawyer, "that the presence of these gentlemen is not altogether useless. You can proceed at once to business," he added, turning to the men.

Cora Leslie wondered at the silent despair of her father.

"Why bow your head, dearest father?" she said, "if your ruin leaves no stain upon your honour. We do not fear poverty. Let us go!"

Craig looked at the Octoroon with a sardonic smile.

"I could have wished that your father had explained to you why you cannot follow him from this place, Miss Leslie," he said; "it will be a painful disclosure for me to make."

"What, sir?" exclaimed Cora, looking alternately from the lawyer to her father.

Gerald Leslie clasped her in his arms.

"My daughter was born in England, Mr. Craig," he said. "She has nothing to do with this business!"

"Your memory fails you this morning, Mr. Leslie," answered Silas; "your daughter was born on this plantation, and is the child of a certain Quadroon slave, called Francilia. The proofs are in my possession."

"What of that?" asked Cora; "what matters whether I was born in England or Louisiana?"

The lawyer took a memorandum-book from his pocket.

"Since your father will not enlighten you, Miss Leslie," he said; "the law must answer your question." He opened the book and read aloud from one of its pages:–

" 'The children of slaves belong to the owner of the mother.' In other words," added the lawyer, as he replaced the book in his pocket, "Mr. Leslie is your master as well as your father; you are, therefore, his property, or that of his creditors."

"Father!" cried Cora, wildly; "do you hear what this man says? You are silent! Oh, Heaven, it is then true!"

For a moment her anguish overcame her; then, turning to Craig, she said:

"What, then, would you do with me, sir?"

"Alas, my poor child," answered Silas, with affected compassion, "you will be sold with the others."

With a shriek of horror the Octoroon buried her face upon her father's breast.

"Sold!" she exclaimed, in a stifled voice; "sold!"

The mulatto Toby stood by, contemplating the scene with mute despair.

"Mr. Craig," said Gerald Leslie, "will not all that I possess suffice to pay the debt I owe you? Why this useless cruelty? Do you fear that the produce of the sale will not be enough to repay you? If it should be so, I swear to you that I will employ the last hour of my life to endeavour to liquidate your claim! If, then, there yet remains one sentiment of pity in your heart, do not rob me of my child?"

"If I were disposed to grant your prayer, Mr. Leslie," answered Silas, "the law is inexorable. All must be sold."

"No, no; who could question your right to do as you please in the matter?"

"You forget," answered the lawyer; "you forget the fifty thousand dollars due to Augustus Horton; I am here to represent his interests as well as my own."

"Augustus Horton," cried Cora; "you hear, father, you hear. It is to deliver me to him that they would separate me from you."

"Re-assure yourself, Miss Leslie," said Silas Craig; "the law requires that the slaves upon a property shall be sold by public auction. That auction will take place at noon to-morrow. Mr. Leslie has only to re-purchase you, – if he can command the means."

But Cora heard him not. The name of Augustus Horton awakened all her terror of the persecution of a base and heartless profligate. She imagined herself already in his power – his slave – his to treat as his vile passion prompted. Wild with terror, she clung convulsively to her father.

"No, no," she cried; "do not abandon me. I shall die; I shall go mad. Do you forget that that man is the murderer of my mother?"

"Silence, silence!" whispered Gerald; "unhappy girl, do not infuriate him."

"I hope, Mr. Leslie," said Craig, as Cora still clung to her father, "that you will not oblige us to have recourse to violence."

"Kill me, kill me, sooner than abandon me to that man," cried Cora.

The mulatto drew a knife from his pocket and handed it to the agonized father.

"Kill her, master," he whispered; "better that than she should meet the fate of her mother."

Gerald pushed the slave from him with a gesture of horror. "No, no!" he exclaimed; "all hope is not yet lost! Between this and to-morrow surely something can be done. I will see Gilbert. We will save you, Cora, my beloved; we will save you."

Two of the men approached the father and daughter to take the Octoroon from Gerald's arms. But Cora only clung to him more convulsively.

"Father, father!" she shrieked.

At a gesture from Craig they seized her in their arms and dragged her away. Happily for the wretched girl, consciousness once more deserted her, and she sank fainting in the arms of the brutal wretches whose business it was to secure her.

Silas Craig looked on at this heart-rending scene with an evil light shining in his red, rat-like eyes.

"For years and years, Mr. Gerald Leslie," he said, "you and the like of you have carried it with a high hand over me. But my turn has come at last, I guess. You look rather small to-day. It's a hard thing for a man to be so poor as to have to sell his favourite daughter."

"Wretch!" cried the agonised father; "this is your hour of triumph; but remember that Heaven suffers such as you to prosper for a while that it may the better confound them in the end. A being capable of infamy such as this must be capable of crime. Guilty deeds long

forgotten are sometimes strangely brought to light, and it may be your
turn to grovel in the dust and ask for mercy of me."

In spite of his hardihood in crime the colour forsook Silas Craig's
face, and left it of a dusky white. The random shot had struck him too
forcibly. The man of guilt trembled.

CHAPTER XXV.
THE STORY OF PAULINE CORSI.

All things went on at the Villa Moraquitos as calmly as if nothing out of
the ordinary course had happened. Camilla and her father met
constantly, and the Spaniard still displayed his absorbing love for his
daughter; but, a few days after the scene in the gambling-house, he
announced to her his intention of making Pauline Corsi his wife.

The young girl's surprise at this announcement knew no bounds.
Nothing could have been more remote from her thoughts than the
possibility of her father's marrying a second time.

She knew of his devotion to her mother – knew the anguish that
had been caused to him by Olympia's early death, and to hear that he
was about to wed the young and frivolous Frenchwoman filled her with
bewilderment.

This, then, was the fulfilment of the ambitious hopes to which
Pauline Corsi had alluded.

Being utterly without avarice or mercenary feelings of any kind,
the announcement of her father's marriage gave no pain to Camilla. On
the contrary, it pleased her to think that he should win a companion for
his declining days, and her only prayer was that Pauline might prove
worthy of his affection, and might learn to make him happy. Her
innocent mind could little dream of the terrible secret which was
involved in this intended marriage. Again, she remembered that no
doubt her fortune would be much reduced by this unlooked-for event;
there would be, therefore, less objection to her union with Paul. This
thought filled her with hope, and she seemed to recognize the hand of
Providence in the turn which events were taking.

But we must retrace our steps, in order to throw a light upon the
timely appearance of Paul Lisimon, Captain Prendergills, and the sailor
Joe, in the secret gambling-house in Columbia Street.

It will be remembered that Camilla Moraquitos had recognized the
copper coloured visage of the sailor in the pit of the crowded
Opera-house.

The beautiful Spanish girl had also been recognized by honest-hearted Joe, whose breast was overflowing with gratitude for the noble handful of dollars which she had only that morning given him.

The Amazon was anchored in the harbour of New Orleans, and Joe had been commissioned by Paul Lisimon to deliver the letter to Camillia, and had at the same time received his Captain's permission to take a night's holiday on shore.

With his pockets full of money the sailor was determined to enjoy himself, and, attracted by the blaze of lights and the brilliant crowd, he strolled into the Opera-house.

Here, the entertainment being not very much to his liking, he amused himself by staring at the audience.

It was then he perceived Camillia Moraquitos. From the moment of recognizing her he scarcely ever took his eyes from the box in which she was seated. Was she not the sweetheart of his Captain's particular friend, the new first mate of the Amazon, and was it not therefore his duty to look after her?

He saw Augustus Horton leaning over Camillia's chair, and immediately set him down as an admirer of the lady, and a rival of Paul Lisimon.

By and bye he saw the planter leave the box to order the carriage at the close of the performance. Determined to watch to the last, he quitted the pit at the same moment, and reached the portico before the theatre in time to see Augustus and Camillia into the carriage that was waiting for them. He also heard the brief dialogue that passed between them at the door of the vehicle.

But the indignation of the honest sailor was unbounded when he saw Augustus take his seat in the carriage by the side of Camillia.

He thought that his Captain's new friend was betrayed, and immediately resolved to know the truth.

As the carriage drove off, he flung himself into the roadway, almost under the hoofs of the horses of other vehicles, in order to follow that which contained Camillia and the planter. In this manner he pursued it until it turned out of the principal thoroughfare.

Then, favoured by the obscurity of the street and the darkness of the night, he sprang forward, and, clambering like a monkey, contrived to seat himself on the board at the back of the vehicle.

He was sufficiently well acquainted with New Orleans to recognize the quarter through which they drove; and when the carriage stopped, he slipped noiselessly from his position, and, lurking in the shadow, watched Camillia and Augustus as they entered the gambling-house. He saw enough to convince him that some description of treachery was on foot, and that, in any case, Paul Lisimon's happiness was in danger.

The carriage drove off without the black coachman having noticed Joe; and the sailor had ample time to examine the exterior of the house, and the street in which it was situated. He recognized the locality as Columbia Street. Then, without a moment's hesitation, he ran to the quay, and got a boat to convey him on board the Amazon. Late as it was, neither Paul nor the Captain had retired to rest. They were both seated in the cabin, with a pile of charts before them, and the young lawyer was taking a lesson in navigation.

Joe lost no time in relating what he had just witnessed; and ten minutes afterwards Paul Lisimon and Captain Prendergills were on shore.

The Captain knew the house on Columbia Street.

"Many a dollar have I lost within its accursed walls," he said, as the three men hurried through the deserted city; "but that's in our favour now, for the keepers of the house know me, and I know the trick of the door, which is a secret only confided to the habitual visitors of the house; so we shall get into the infernal den without any difficulty, and once in, we'll find out what all this means, and whether Don Juan's daughter is deceiving you."

"She deceive me!" exclaimed Paul, indignantly; "she is all truth, all purity; but if the man who was with her is he whom I imagine, she is the victim of treachery as vile as that from which I am a sufferer."

Thanks to Captain Prendergills, they had no difficulty in penetrating the mysterious building. A man, seated in a little anteroom on the stairs took their hats from them, and told them which way to go to the gambling-saloons; but at the very moment they reached the top of the principal staircase the thrilling shriek of Camillia Moraquitos echoed through the house.

The ear of Paul Lisimon, sharpened by anxiety, told him whence this shriek proceeded. It came from a long corridor to their left.

They rushed down this corridor, and burst open the door at the end as a second shriek pealed through the building.

The result is already known to the reader.

The letter written by Silas Craig, which summoned Don Juan Moraquitos from the opera-box, was a part of the planter's base plot, and had been planned between him and the lawyer. The business relations between Silas and Don Juan were so complicated that it was easy for the artful attorney to occupy the Spaniard in discussing them till long after midnight. The two men sat talking till nearly three o'clock in that very apartment ornamented with the map of the United States, and communicating with the gambling-house in Columbia Street.

But the two houses were separated by a passage of considerable length, and Don Juan was too far from his beloved daughter to hear that terrible shriek of distress which alarmed every player at the gaming table.

* * * * * * * *

Upon the day on which Silas Craig, accompanied by the limbs of the law, entered the house of Gerald Leslie, taking with him desolation and anguish, Pauline Corsi and Camillia Moraquitos were once more seated in the boudoir of the Spanish girl.

The Amazon had sailed from New Orleans, carrying Paul Lisimon away from danger of apprehension – away also from her he loved.

Matters were rapidly drawing towards a crisis – within a few days the French governess was to become the bride of Juan Moraquitos.

But the wealthy Spaniard had little of the aspect of a happy bridegroom. He rarely entered the apartments of either his daughter or Pauline Corsi, but he spent his hours in gloomy meditation in his study, and admitted no one to his presence.

Camillia was cruelly distressed by this change, yet she dared not interrogate the haughty Spaniard. Sometimes she imagined that he reproached himself for contracting a second alliance which might lessen his daughter's wealth.

"If he knew how little I care for the gold which others so value," she thought; "if he knew how happy I could be in the humblest home shared with those I love, he would not fear to rob me of a few thousands."

The confidence commenced between Camillia and Pauline upon the day of Augustus Horton's plotted defeat had never been discontinued, and it was to the Frenchwoman alone that Camillia looked for hope and comfort.

Strange anomaly of human nature! The ambitious and unscrupulous being who could stoop to purchase a wealthy husband by means of a vile and guilty secret, had yet some better feelings left. Pauline loved her pupil – loved her with the light love of a selfish nature it is true, but it is something that one spark of affection remained in her perverted nature.

"You are sad, Camillia?" she said, as she looked up from her embroidery frame to watch the thoughtful face of the Spanish girl.

Camillia was seated with her hands lying idle in her lap, her eyes fixed vacantly upon the river, shining through the open window.

"You are sad, Camillia?" repeated Pauline.

Camillia aroused herself as if with an effort.

"Can I be otherwise," she said, "when I think of him? When I remember that he is away, I know not where, his name branded with disgrace, a wanderer and an outcast."

"Silly child! Have I not already told you that the day which crowns my ambition shall also crown your love?"

"Oh, Pauline! If I could but believe you!" sighed Camillia.

"And can you not believe me? Do I look like one who has no will to accomplish her wish? Look in my face, and see if there is one line that tells of weakness there?"

Camillia raised her eyes to the face of her late governess with an earnest and wondering gaze.

Youthful as was that countenance, delicate as were the features and complexion, brilliant though the azure of the eyes, there was a look of decision, a glance of determination rarely seen in the faces of strong men. There was a power for good or evil – terrible, incalculable, if employed for the latter – the power of a great intellect and an unyielding will.

"Pauline!" exclaimed Camillia, "you are an enigma."

"Not so," answered the governess, her clear blue eyes dilating, her lip quivering with suppressed emotion. "Not so, Camillia; I am an injured woman."

"Injured!"

"Yes. You, whose life has been smooth as yonder river, sleeping beneath the sunshine that gilds its breast – you have never known what it is to writhe beneath a sense of injury – to feel that your whole existence has been blighted by the crimes of others. There are wrongs that can transform an angel to a fiend; so do not wonder when you see me cold, heartless, ambitious, designing. My nature was poisoned by the events of my youth. I said that I would one day tell you my story. Shall I tell it you now?"

"Yes, Pauline, yes; if it is not painful to you."

"It *is* painful; but I feel a savage pleasure in the pain. I gnash my teeth at the remembrance of the old and bitter wrongs; but I love to recall them, for the thought of them makes me strong. Have you ever wondered at my past history, Camillia?"

"Never."

"I was born beneath a princely roof, cradled in the luxury of a palace; the man I called my father was a duke – the woman, whose gorgeous beauty smiled upon my infancy, was a duchess!"

"They were your parents?" exclaimed Camillia.

"I was taught to think so. They were of the Italian race, and sprang from one of the most powerful families of the South – a family whose pride had become a proverb throughout Italy. They had been married for some years, and had grown weary of hoping for an heir to the ancient name which, if they had died without posterity, would have become extinct. Disappointed in his hope of perpetuating his noble race, the duke had grown indifferent to his beautiful wife; nay, something worse than indifference had arisen – something bordering on dislike, which, in spite of his efforts, he was unable to conceal. The duchess came of a house almost as noble as that of her husband. She was a haughty and imperious woman, and she was not slow to perceive this change in the manner of the duke. She discovered, that in the very prime of her youth and beauty, she was despised by her husband. The bitterness of this discovery changed her very nature. Every day she grew more haughty, more exacting, more capricious. She shut herself from the gay world in which she had been admired, and abandoned herself to a mute but terrible despair."

"Poor woman, she suffered!" murmured Camillia.

"She did! She was wronged, but it did not make her more pitiful to others when their time of suffering came. It hardened her nature, and made her merciless, as all injustice must ever do. The duke observed this gloomy silence – this dumb despair. He could not restore to her an affection which he no longer felt; but he sought to revive her spirits by change of scene, and by those hollow pleasures which are the sole resource of the idle."

"Vain solace! Poor lady, she was indeed to be pitied."

"Ay, but her haughty soul would have rejected pity as the direst wrong. The duke left Italy, and took her to Paris, where, in the midst of the gay and frivolous, she might forget her domestic griefs; but in France, as in Italy, she refused to share in the pleasures of the world of rank and fashion, and obstinately shut herself in her own chamber."

"Yet she did not die! Strange that such sorrow could not kill!"

"Sorrow does not kill. Even her beauty suffered no diminution. It was still in the full splendour of its luxuriance, dark, proud, commanding, queen-like. Have you ever heard, Camillia Moraquitos, of the secrets of Paris? Have you ever heard of the mysteries of that wonderful city, in which almost every street has its secret, known only to the initiated in the winding ways of civilized life? Three months after the arrival of the duke and duchess in Paris, an event occurred which changed the whole current of their lives."

"And that event was—"

"Apparently a very simple one; the lady's-maid of the duchess was a frivolous girl, who had herself been educated in France, but who had never before tasted the delights of the brilliant capital. She was intoxicated with rapture, and she ventured even to express her admiration for Paris in the presence of the young duchess. Amongst the other wonders of this marvellous city, Jeannette, as the girl was called, spoke of a fortune-teller who had related to her some of the events of her past life, and whom she looked upon as a powerful magician."

"But surely the duchess did not listen to this peasant girl's foolish babble."

"She did! Despair is, perhaps, terribly near akin to madness. She listened at first from pure abstraction, scarce heeding what she heard; but afterwards eagerly. She asked the girl a thousand questions about this fortune-teller, and finally it was agreed upon between the mistress and maid that the woman should visit the duchess late on the following night, when the duke was absent at a political assembly, and all the servants of the establishment had retired to rest."

"Strange caprice!" exclaimed Camillia.

"Grief is sometimes capricious. The duchess, doubtless, was ashamed of her own folly, but she wished to hear what this woman would say of the future, which seemed so dark. What if she were to prophesy the coming of an heir to that haughty house – an heir whose coming would restore all the power of the now neglected wife? The duchess passed the following day in a state of restless excitement, eager for the coming hour which would bring the fortune-teller.

"It was nearly midnight when Jeannette admitted the woman by a private door at the bottom of the grand staircase.

"There was something terrible in the look of the woman who crept with stealthy and silent tread over the luxurious carpets of that palace-like abode. She was old and haggard; her yellow skin disfigured by innumerable wrinkles; her grey hair falling in elf locks about her low and narrow forehead. Her small eyes were surrounded by red and inflamed circles, and almost hidden by the bushy eyebrows which projected over them. Her chin was fringed with terrible grey bristles; her mouth disfigured by two enormous teeth, which resembled the fangs of a wild beast. She was a creature calculated to inspire disgust and terror, and she seemed still more horrible by contrast with the elegance around her, as she entered the superb apartments of the duchess.

"There is little doubt that the maid, Jeannette, had told this woman all the secrets of her mistress. Her task, therefore, was an easy one. She described the troubles of the past, and foretold that, before the year had elapsed, a child would be born to the duke and duchess. On hearing this prophecy from the lips of a miserable impostor, the haughty Italian fell at her feet, and burst into an hysterical flood of tears. The woman saw in that moment the first dim foreshadowing of a future crime. A week afterwards she came again at the same hour. This time she saw the duchess alone, and remained with her for so long a period that Jeannette's curiosity was excited. She contrived to overhear the interview.

"Once more the duchess seemed a transformed being. She no longer shut herself from the world. Gay and radiant she re-entered society; and in a few months the duke was informed that he would ere long become a father.

"On hearing this he was eager for an immediate return to Italy, in order that the infant might be born upon the soil which it was by and bye to inherit; but the duchess had a strange caprice upon this point. She was determined not to leave Paris, and her husband could not bring himself to oppose her wishes at such a time.

"Within a twelvemonth from the first visit of the fortune-teller, a child was born and reared in the ducal mansion. I was that child. Caressed and indulged from my earliest infancy, nursed in luxury and elegance, I was happy, for I had much of the frivolous nature of my native Paris; but, child as I was, I knew that I was not beloved. I saw the looks of other women as they hung over their children, and I knew that such glances of affection never rested upon me. The duke loaded me with presents, but he never embraced me as I had seen other fathers embrace their children, and I felt that some gem was wanting in the diadem of happiness. Years passed; I grew to early girlhood, and for the first time I knew what it was to love. A young artist, who had been engaged to paint my portrait, fell in love with me, and his passion was returned. For the first and only time I too loved; devotedly, enduringly. The painter, though handsome, honourable, high-minded, distinguished, was driven from that ducal mansion with scorn and contumely. What greater sin could he have committed? He had dared to love the daughter of one of Italy's proudest noblemen.

"This was the first bitter wrong of my life. The pride of others trampled on my hopes of happiness, and at sixteen years of age my breast was embittered by a blighted affection. My lover wrote me a letter of despairing farewell and left the country for America. To this day I know not to what part of the mighty continent he went."

"Poor Pauline!"

"A twelvemonth after this, Jeannette, the servant of the duchess, died; and on her death-bed she sent for the duke and confided to him a terrible secret. I was not the daughter of a duchess, but a spurious child, born of low parents, and introduced into the ducal mansion by the old Parisian fortune-teller."

"Oh, Heaven, how terrible!"

"It was indeed terrible. The fury of the duke knew no bounds. He was a proud man, and for seventeen years he had been duped, fooled, imposed upon by the child of some wretched Frenchwoman – the child he had introduced into the society of the noblest in the land, and whose beauty and accomplishments had been his boast. He had never loved me; there was no link of affection between us to stay the torrent of his rage. That rage was more terrific against me, the innocent! than even towards the guilty duchess. He drove me from his doors with loathing, and I, the pampered heiress, wandered forth into the streets of Genoa, a beggar and an outcast. Before I reached the gates of the town I was overtaken by the steward of the duke, who brought me a pocket-book from his master. It contained notes to the amount of three thousand pounds. My first impulse was to cast it in the dirt beneath my feet, and to bid the steward go back and tell his lord how I had treated his generous donation; but a sudden idea took possession of me. This sum of money would enable me to go where I pleased. I might go to America – I might find him I loved. Two months after this I landed in New York. I travelled from city to city, but nowhere could I obtain tidings of him I sought; and at last, wearied by my ineffectual search, my funds nearly exhausted with the extravagant outlay of my travels, I found myself in New Orleans. You know the rest."

CHAPTER XXVI.
THE SLAVE SALE.

THE SLAVE SALE

At twelve o'clock upon the day after that on which Gerald Leslie and his daughter had been parted by the pitiless attorney, the slave auction commenced.

The sale was to take place in a public auction room in New Orleans; an apartment capable of containing upwards of a hundred people. At one end of this room stood the rostrum of the auctioneer, while immediately before his desk was stretched a long table of rough deal, upon which one by one the slaves took their places, while the auctioneer expatiated upon their merits. Round this table was placed benches, on which the buyers and lookers-on lounged during the auction.

The plantation hands were the first to be sold, and the sale had lasted for some hours when Toby, the mulattto, slowly mounted the table, and took his stand before the eager eyes of the buyers.

The countenance of the slave was sad and careworn; and, as he ascended the table, he looked anxiously round the room as if seeking amongst all those eager faces for some one he expected to see there.

But it was evident that he looked in vain, for, after a long and earnest scrutiny of that varied crowd, he sighed heavily, and his head sank upon his breast with a gesture of despair. The bidding lasted for some time, and the most persevering bidder was Silas Craig himself, who sat on a bench close to the table, and amused himself by whittling a stick with his bowie knife. One by one the other purchasers gave way, and the mulatto fell to the attorney.

As the hammer of the auctioneer descended upon the desk, thus proclaiming that the bargain was complete, a singular expression illuminated the face of the slave, Toby.

That expression seemed one of mingled hate and triumph; and, as he descended from the platform, the hand of the mulatto mechanically sought for some object hidden in his breast.

That object was the knife with which Francilia had stabbed herself – the knife which Toby had offered the day before to Gerald Leslie.

The mulatto slowly withdrew into a corner where some other slaves purchased by Silas Craig were huddled together, awaiting the termination of the sale.

For some moments there was a pause. Several amongst the crowd asked what the next lot was to be.

The voice of the auctioneer responded from his rostrum, "The Octoroon girl, Cora!"

Again there was a pause. There were few there who did not know the story of Gerald Leslie and his daughter, and every one present seemed to draw a long breath.

The Octoroon emerged from a group of slaves, behind whom she had been hidden, and slowly ascended the platform.

Never in her happiest day – never when surrounded by luxury, when surfeited by adulation and respect, had Cora Leslie looked more lovely than to-day.

Her face was whiter than marble, her large dark eyes were shrouded beneath their drooping lids, fringed with long and silken lashes; her rich wealth of raven hair had been loosened by the rude hands of an overseer, and fell in heavy masses far below her waist; her slender yet rounded figure was set off by the soft folds of her simple cambric dress, which displayed her shoulders and arms in all their statuesque beauty.

One murmur of admiration spread through the assembly as the Octoroon took her place upon the table.

All there had heard of the loveliness of Gerald Leslie's daughter, yet few had expected to see her so lovely.

Eyeglasses were raised, spectacles put on, and looks of insolent admiration were fixed upon the unhappy girl.

But she saw them not – the centre of every eye, she was scarcely conscious of how much she had to endure. Her whole being was absorbed in one thought. Her father; would he come, would he rescue her?

When for one brief instant she lifted her eyes, the crowd of faces swam before her, as if hidden from her by a veil of mist. The sounds of the many voices fell as confused murmurs upon her ears. She was listening for the voice which should announce to her that help was near. But that longed-for voice did not come, and she heard instead the harsh accents of the auctioneer dwelling upon the charms which were to be sold to the highest bidder.

At this moment two men entered the building from opposite doors.

One of these was Augustus Horton, the other Gilbert Margrave.

Gerald Leslie and the engineer had passed a night of utter wretchedness. All the ready money that the ruined planter could command consisted of a few thousand dollars, and Gilbert Margrave had only the sum which he had brought with him for his travelling expenses. To communicate with England was impossible, though the young man had ample resources there; he had also letters of credit on a banking-house in New York, but he well knew that nothing but ready money could save Cora from her infamous persecutors. The entire sum at his command was a little over twenty thousand dollars.

Gilbert Margrave was the first to bid.

"Five thousand dollars!"

"Six thousand!" cried Augustus Horton.

A laugh circulated amongst the assembly. "I guess you begun a bit too low, stranger," said one of the planters.

"Seven thousand."

"Ten!" cried Augustus.

"Guess we'll teach you what a slave sale is, Britisher," said another man near Gilbert, cutting a lump of tobacco and thrusting it into his mouth.

Gilbert Margrave's cheek grew pale; he felt that the man he had to deal with was not to be beaten.

"Twelve thousand," – "fifteen," – "twenty."

For a moment there was a pause; Gilbert drew his breath. For one brief instant he thought that the planter's caprice might be less powerful than his avarice. He knew not that Augustus Horton's love for Cora was full of passionate determination.

"Five and twenty thousand dollars," cried the planter.

Gilbert was silent. Throughout this scene the Octoroon had never once lifted her eyes from the ground; but, at this ominous silence, she slowly raised them, and looked imploringly at her lover.

It was a glance of despair which answered this mute appeal. All hope was over.

"Strikes me you're pretty well cleaned out, sirree," said one of the men who had spoken before.

The bidding continued, the excitement of the scene had become intense. Thirty, five and thirty, forty thousand dollars were bid; forty five, fifty thousand.

The last bid came from Augustus Horton, and the auctioneer's hammer descended with an ominous sound.

Cora was his.

Gilbert Margrave sprang forward, as if he would have struck the planter, but a friendly hand was laid upon his shoulder, and he was dragged back by a group of Americans.

"Better keep your dander down, stranger," one of the men whispered in his ear, "our folks are not over fond of your countrymen just now, and they wouldn't make much work of taking out their bowie knives. Let him have the gal. Was there ever such a noise about a handsome slave?"

Augustus Horton walked up to the place where Gilbert was standing, surrounded by these men.

"I've beaten you before to-day, Mr. Margrave," he said, with a sneer, "and I think I've had the pleasure of giving you a second licking this afternoon."

Again Gilbert would have sprung upon him, but again he was restrained by those about him.

"We've another duel to fight yet, Mr. Horton," said the Englishman, "and in that you may not come off so easily."

"We citizens of New Orleans don't fight about coloured gals," answered the planter, turning upon his heel, contemptuously, and walking towards the spot where Cora stood, side by side with Toby and the other slaves.

Gilbert Margrave released himself from the arms of those who held him. "I must follow him," he said, "I must speak to him. I pledge you my honour that I will attempt no violence, but I tell you I must speak to him. Life and death hang on this matter. How can I go back to Gerald Leslie, and tell the broken-hearted father that I was powerless to save his only child?"

Gilbert found Augustus standing at a little distance from the group of slaves, contemplating Cora with the insolently admiring glance with which the master surveys his property.

She was no longer the woman who had scorned and defied him. She was his slave, his purchased slave, over whom the law gave him full and indisputable authority.

"Mr. Horton," said Gilbert, in a voice rendered hoarse by emotion, "let me speak to you for a few moments?"

The planter bowed superciliously. "Well, sir?" he said, as they withdrew to a solitary corner of the auction room.

"You are aware that had my means enabled me, I would have outbid you just now in the purchase of Miss Leslie."

Augustus Horton laughed aloud.

"Miss Leslie!" he repeated scornfully; "we don't call the slaves Miss and Mr. down south. I guess you would like to outbid me for this Octoroon girl, Cora, but I'm happy to say you weren't able to do it. Had you bid a hundred thousand dollars, I'd have outbid you, and if you'd doubled that I'd have outbid you still. No man comes cheaply between Augustus Horton and his will."

"Tell me," said Gilbert, "tell me, what do you want with Mr. Leslie's daughter. Why do you want to become her master?"

Again Augustus laughed, and the hot blood mounted to Gilbert's cheek as he heard the mocking laughter.

"If it comes to that," said the planter, "why do you want her?"

"Because I love her."

"Then one answer will do for both of us," said Augustus. "I want her because I love her."

"No," cried Gilbert, "no, Mr. Horton. Do not sully the pure and holy name of Love by so base a blasphemy. Yours is the low passion of the profligate who seeks to destroy that which he pretends to love. Mine is the honourable sentiment of the man who seeks to bestow upon her he adores the sacred name of wife."

"You Britishers have another way of thinking to what we have in Louisiana," answered Augustus; "we don't marry our slaves. However, I've no wish to quarrel with other folks' opinions; the girl's mine and I don't mean to part with her, so good day to you, Mr. Margrave."

Gilbert laid his hand upon the planter's shoulder.

"One moment," he said. "The sum which I offered just now for Miss Leslie was the extent of the ready money I possess; but it was not one twentieth part of what I can command. Communication with London, or even with New York, will bring me the funds I require. I ask you – as a gentleman appealing to a gentleman, upon a subject that is dearer to him than life – I ask you to do a great and generous action. Accept my note of hand for a hundred thousand dollars; double the sum you have just given – and let me restore Cora Leslie to her father?"

Augustus Horton shrugged his shoulders.

"I would be very glad to oblige you, Mr. Margrave," he said; "but as I don't happen to want money just now, and as I've a fancy for keeping the Octoroon, I beg to decline your liberal offer."

Gilbert Margrave glanced at him with a scornful smile.

"I appealed to you as a gentleman," he said. "I was mistaken. You shall hear from me to-night."

CHAPTER XXVII.
THE EVE OF THE WEDDING.

On the night of the slave sale, Don Juan Moraquitos sat alone in the apartment which he called his study.

The following day was that appointed for the Spaniard's marriage with Pauline Corsi, and preparations had been made for the celebration of the ceremony with the splendour worthy of such a wealthy bridegroom. Pauline and Camillia were together in the young girl's apartments. On one of the sofas lay the dresses of white satin and lace, which the bride and bride's-maid were to wear upon the following morning. On a table near stood a box, which contained the wreaths selected by the Frenchwoman for herself and Camillia.

This box had not as yet been opened.

"Come, dearest Camillia," exclaimed Pauline; "have you no wish to see the Parisian flowers which are to adorn that beautiful head to-morrow? You certainly are most devoid of that feminine weakness – curiosity."

"I can trust to your taste, Pauline," answered Camillia.

"That's just as much as to say you don't care a straw about the matter; and that you are thinking of nothing but that stupid lover of yours, who is, no doubt, thousands and thousands of miles away."

Camillia sighed. Her face was averted, and she did not see the arch smile which lighted up the Frenchwoman's face. "However," continued Pauline; "I shall insist on your approving of my choice."

She unfastened the cord which was tied about the box; and, lifting the lid, took out the two wreaths.

They were both of the same pattern – coronet-shaped garlands of orange flowers and buds, purely white amidst their glistening green leaves; as true to nature as if they had been gathered from a hothouse, and breathing the delicious perfume of the flower. They were the perfection of Parisian taste and art.

"Why, Pauline," exclaimed Camillia, "they are both bridal wreaths."

"Can you guess why that it is?"

"No, indeed."

"Because there will be two brides to-morrow. I never break a promise. To-morrow, Don Juan Moraquitos will divide his fortune; one half he will reserve for himself and his wife, the other he will give to his daughter and the husband of her choice."

"But, Pauline, how in Heaven's name will you accomplish this?"

"That is my secret. There is very little time left me for my work. It is now nine o'clock, I must go out immediately."

"Go out, and at this hour?"

"It is absolutely necessary."

"But, dear Pauline, you will have my carriage, you will let me accompany you?"

"Neither; I go on foot and alone."

She hurried from the room before Camillia could remonstrate further, and the Spanish girl, bewildered and amazed, seated herself near the table, looking musingly at the two bridal wreaths.

That night Silas Craig sat alone in the office in which was the map of America. The lawyer had triumphed over the man who had scorned him. He had seen Gerald Leslie's proud nature abased to the very dust, and the darling child of a doting father sold to her most deadly enemy; for the slave has no greater enemy than the hardened profligate, whose guilty passions her charms have awakened. Silas Craig was a winner in the game of life – what cared he for dark secrets upon the cards he had played? He was rich, and he could defy mankind.

He had dined sumptuously after the fatigue of the slave sale, and the table before him was spread with glittering decanters of the choicest wines. This man revelled in the luxuries of a palace; but he had risen from the gutter; and his low and grovelling soul still wore the degradation of the foul haunts in which he had been reared. He lounged in his easy chair, sipping wine, which sparkled like melted jewels in the light of the shaded lamp. He was disturbed from his reverie by the entrance of the slave who waited upon him.

"A lady, massa," said the man.

"A lady! a lady at this time of night? pshaw; why you must be dreaming."

"No, massa, me wide awake. A lady, a very beautiful lady, with white hands and rings, oh, golly! dey shine like stars."

"Did she tell you her name?"

"No, massa, but she gib me dis."

The negro handed Silas a card.

This card bore the name of Mdlle. Pauline Corsi.

Beneath the card was written this warning:–

"There are secrets which Silas Craig may wish to preserve; if so, he will do well to see Mdlle. Corsi."

Like all base creatures, Silas was a coward. The card dropped from his trembling hand, and his bloated face grew ashy pale.

"Admit the lady," he said.

The slave left the room, and in a few minutes returned with Pauline Corsi.

During those few brief moments, Silas Craig had recovered from his first impulse of terror. What could this woman know of his secrets? Who was she but the paid dependent of Don Juan Moraquitos? He had nothing to fear, therefore. All the native insolence of his nature returned, and when the governess entered the room, he neither rose from his seat nor offered her a chair.

The impertinence did not escape Pauline Corsi. With a smile of provoking assurance, she seated herself opposite to the lawyer, and threw back the dark veil that had shaded her face.

"We shall understand one another better, by-and-bye, Mr. Craig," she said, quietly.

"May I ask the motive of this rather untimely visit?"

"We will come to that in good time, my dear sir," replied Pauline, laughing; "perhaps there are several motives. Suppose then, that we begin with motive number one."

The lawyer writhed beneath her calm assurance.

"I must tell you, Mademoiselle," he said, "that these ain't my business hours, and that if you've anything particular to say to me, you'd better call another time. Though I should think," he added insolently, "that the governess of Don Juan Moraquitos can't have much business with lawyers."

"But the wife of Don Juan Moraquitos may, Mr. Craig."

"The wife!"

"Yes, I see your client does not give you his entire confidence. I am to become Pauline Moraquitos before twelve o'clock to-morrow."

The lawyer's cheek once more grew ashy pale. Again a sudden terror seized him. He felt that there was some mystery shrouded beneath this business, of which he now heard for the first time.

"I know the question which very naturally rises to your lips," said Pauline, with quiet deliberation. "You would ask what motive can have induced Don Juan Moraquitos to take such a step. I reply to that question before it is asked. *The motive is a most powerful one.*"

Silas quailed beneath the look which accompanied these emphatic words. Pauline Corsi had not boasted idly of the power of her will.

The guilty lawyer, versed in every art of lying and chicanery, trembled, he scarce knew why, in the presence of this frail girl.

"Do you ask the nature of this motive?" said Pauline.

"I do," he faltered, pouring out a glass of wine. His hand shook so violently that the neck of the decanter rattled against the rim of the glass, and he spilled half the costly liquid as he raised it to his quivering lips.

He had no reason to fear this Frenchwoman – but the strength of her indomitable will had a magnetic power over him, and his brutal nature bowed beneath its force.

"I will tell you, Silas Craig," answered Pauline; "there are some secrets which, once known, give to the person who discovers them a fearful and a boundless power over the guilty wretches whom they concern. Secrets that are discovered when least the criminals fear detection. Words that are overheard, and cherished for years by the person who overhears them. Words which have power to drag the guilty to the scaffold; words that can kill. Do you understand me?"

"No."

He spoke doggedly, but sat with his hands clasped upon the arms of his easy-chair, his rat-like eyes almost starting from his head as he gazed at Pauline.

"Think again, Silas Craig," said the Frenchwoman; "surely I have spoken plainly. Can you not understand me?"

"No," he repeated with a terrible oath.

"I must speak more plainly still then, it appears. Silas Craig, thirteen years ago it was my good fortune to become acquainted with such a secret as this!"

The lawyer raised one of his trembling hands and wiped the cold perspiration from his icy forehead.

"Thirteen years ago," he muttered.

"Yes; I see you remember the date. I was a penniless girl of seventeen when I discovered this secret. I am now thirty; I have kept it long and patiently, have I not?"

He did not answer her.

"*I have waited my time*! I knew that this secret would bring me wealth and power whenever it was told. It concerns two men. Those two men are my slaves! At a word from me, they stand before the tribunals of this city branded with crime – loathed by their fellow citizens. A word from me, and they go from homes of luxury to the gloom of a prison, from which but a few steps will lead them to the gallows. Shall I tell you who those two men are, Silas Craig?"

"If you please."

He tried to speak with his accustomed insolent and mocking smile, but the white lips refused to do his will, and his words came in a hollow whisper.

"The first is Don Juan Moraquitos, the second is – you!"

The word seemed to whistle from her lips like the bullet from a pistol. The lawyer fell back in his chair as if he had received a blow.

"The secret concerns the night upon which Tomaso Crivelli died, and the will which on that night was forged by you, after the real will had been made away with. The secret also concerns the young man called Paul Lisimon. The man whom you dared to accuse of theft."

"How – how did you discover this?"

"No matter how. Enough that I did make the discovery. Shall I tell you now the price I ask for my secret?"

"Yes."

All attempt at insolence or defiance upon the part of the lawyer was now abandoned. Silas Craig cowered before the Frenchwoman as humbly as the criminal who awaits the sentence of his judge.

"Don Juan Moraquitos will make me his wife and will share with me his own fortune. From him I ask no more than this. We shall leave America for Paris, and in the delight of my native city I shall endeavour to forget the sorrows of my youth. But although I am ambitious, I am not utterly selfish, and in my triumph I wish to secure the happiness of others. Those others are Camillia Moraquitos and the young man it has pleased Don Juan to call Paul Lisimon."

"How do they concern me?" asked Silas.

"You shall hear. By a foul and infamous plot, the details of which I do not know, but which is doubtless worthy of the person who has concocted it, you have contrived to brand the name of Paul Lisimon with infamy. You will reveal that plot. You will withdraw that shameful accusation; and you will insert an advertisement in every paper printed in New Orleans declaring the young man's innocence. You may call your plot a practical joke if you please. You are so universally beloved and respected that you will of course be believed. That is my first condition. Do you comply with it?"

Silas Craig bent his head. He had scarcely power to speak.

"My second demand is that you produce the *real* will, signed by Don Tomaso Crivelli, in which he leaves the whole of his estate to his only and legitimate son, Paul Crivelli, known in this city as Paul Lisimon."

Again the lawyer bent his head.

"In conjunction with Don Juan Moraquitos, you will restore to this young man the wealth of his father, which you divided into equal portions soon after Don Tomaso's death. You will find no difficulty with Juan Moraquitos. Pirate and adventurer, as he has been, he is not so fortunate as you. He has still a conscience."

"Is that all?" gasped the lawyer.

"It is. I think we understand each other a little better now than we did half-an-hour ago. Good night."

She left the room before he could reply, and before he could summon the negro to usher her from the house.

It was nearly eleven o'clock when Pauline Corsi left the lawyer's office, but the streets were lighted brilliantly by the full moon which sailed high in the heavens. The Frenchwoman drew her veil closely over her face. She was dressed in dark garments, which shielded her from observation, and she hurried rapidly through the lonely streets.

About half way towards her destination she met two men walking side by side, smoking cigars.

Suddenly she stopped, and, clasping her hand upon her heart, looked eagerly at the younger of these two men.

"It cannot be," she murmured; "it cannot be. It is the moonlight which deceives me."

At this moment they drew near a tavern, the door of which was brilliantly lighted.

The lamp-light fell upon the face of the younger man.

The two men entered the tavern, and Pauline Corsi remained a few paces from the threshold, looking after them.

"Can I be mistaken?" she said, "and yet it seems like some bewildering dream. I might – after thirteen weary years – and to-night!"

CHAPTER XXVIII.
THE ABDUCTION.

CORA DEFIES HER MASTER

The same moonlight which illumined the meeting of Pauline Corsi and the strangers in the streets of New Orleans, shone on the smooth bosom of the Mississippi, and on the white walls of the villa residence of Augustus Horton.

The house and plantation of Hortonville were some miles from the wood in which the duel between Augustus and Gilbert had taken place. The scenery which surrounded the villa was exquisitely beautiful, and the building itself, seen beneath the light of the moon, with its lamp-lit windows gleaming like pale gems in the glory of the summer's night, had the appearance of some fairy palace rather than any earthly habitation.

You might almost have expected to see those white walls melt into thin air and fade away from your gaze.

It was nearly midnight, and the planter's small household had retired to rest. There were only two watchers in that luxurious habitation. The first of these was Augustus Horton; the second was Cora, the Octoroon.

The unhappy girl had been brought from the auction-room to Hortonville in Augustus's phaeton, the thoroughbred horses of which made brief work of the journey from New Orleans.

Adelaide Horton and her aunt, Mrs. Montresor, were still at their city residence. Cora scarce dared to think why Augustus had chosen to take her to Hortonville, rather than to his town house.

The answer to that question was too terrible. Could there be any doubt as to his motive in choosing this lonely villa for the retreat of the Octoroon? Was it not that the wretched girl might be more fully in his power?

The chamber to which Cora had been conducted was even more luxuriously furnished than her own tastefully decorated apartment in the pavilion on the borders of Lake Pont Chartrain, but the Octoroon looked at the splendour around her with a shudder. She knew that it was not thus that slaves were ordinarily treated, and she knew the sinister meaning of this seeming kindness.

The young mulattress who led Cora to her apartment informed her that she had been appointed to wait upon Miss Leslie.

Cora smiled bitterly.

"Who told you to call me, Miss Leslie?" she asked.

"My master, Mr. Horton."

"Alas, my poor girl," answered Cora, "I am no longer Miss Leslie. I am a slave like yourself, with no name save that which my master chooses to give me. He has bought me; bought me at the auction yonder. Name, fame, happiness, honour, ay, and even soul – as he thinks – are his."

In the bitterness of her despair she buried her face in her hands and sobbed aloud.

The mulattress was touched to the heart by this burst of grief.

"My dear mistress, pray do not weep thus," she said. "You will be no slave here, I know, for our master has had these beautiful rooms prepared on purpose for you, and you are to be treated as a queen."

"A queen!" said Cora, hysterically. "Yes, the empress of a profligate's hour of pleasure, to be trampled beneath his feet when the whim has passed. Go, my good girl; why should I distress you with my griefs. You can never understand my misery."

It was impossible, indeed, for this poor ignorant slave to comprehend the feelings of the highly educated and refined woman, torn from a father she adored, and from him who was to have rescued her from slavery and made her a happy English wife.

Cora dried her tears; and, affecting a calmness which she did not feel, dismissed the mulattress.

The girl had lighted a shaded lamp upon an elegant little inlaid table, and had brought a tray loaded with delicacies for Cora's refreshment, but the Octoroon turned with a sickened heart from the rich food set before her. She had eaten nothing that day, and her lips and throat were parched and burning with inward fever. She poured out a glass of iced water and drained the cool liquid to the last drop. Then, throwing open the wide Venetian shutters, she looked out into the calm night.

What if there were yet hope? What if she could escape?

A thrill vibrated through her inmost soul as she asked herself these questions.

She fell on her knees, and lifting her clasped hands, exclaimed in an outburst of enthusiasm,–

"Oh, Merciful and Beneficent Creator! I cannot believe that Thou wouldst utterly abandon the meanest of thy creatures. Even here, on the brink of terrors more hideous than the most cruel death, I still hope, I still believe, that Thou wilt show me a way of deliverance!"

The Octoroon rose from her knees, a new creature after the utterance of this heartfelt prayer. Her very countenance seemed as if transfigured by the sublime emotions of the moment. A holy light shone from her tearless eyes; a faint flush of crimson relieved the pallor of her cheek.

"My father abandons me to my fate. Even he who was to be my husband can do no more to save me. It is to Heaven, then, that I turn, and to One above who is stronger than all earthly friends."

The apartment to which Cora had been conducted was on the upper floor of the villa; but the ceilings of the lower chambers were far from lofty, and the window from which the Octoroon looked was scarcely eleven feet from the ground. Under this window ran a rustic colonnade with slender pilasters, round which hung the leaves and blossoms of the luxuriant creeping plants familiar to the South. The roof of this colonnade formed a balcony before Cora's window.

For some moments the Octoroon stood at the open casement, gazing on the scene beneath her and lost in thought.

"If I remain in this house," she murmured, "I am utterly in the power of that base man. Another moment, and he may enter this chamber; again I may hear those words which are poison to my soul; and this time he may force me to listen to his infamous proposals. All those beneath this roof are the slaves of his will – it were hopeless, then, to look for help from them, but beneath that purple vault, I might surely be safer; and at the worst the river is near at hand."

She shuddered as she spoke. To this girl, religiously educated, there was something horrible in the idea of suicide. It seemed a doubt of Providence even to think of this worst and last resource.

But on one thing she had determined, and that was to escape from the house to the gardens below; once there, she might find her way to some adjoining plantation, where she might meet with some benevolent creature who would interfere to shield her from her hated master.

It was not slavery she feared, it was dishonour.

The rope with which she had been bound still hung to one of her wrists. This rope might be the means of saving her.

She examined the door of her chamber and found that it was locked on the outside.

"So much the better," she thought; "he believes his prisoner to be safe. He thinks that I would not dare a leap of a few feet even to escape from him. How little he knows of a woman's power in the moment of desperation!"

She hurried to the balcony, and attached the cord, which was about five feet long, to the iron railing, then with the help of this cord she dropped lightly to the ground.

She alighted unhurt upon the soft earth of a flower-bed, but the slender rope had broken with her weight, and the best part of it remained in her hand.

She was free!

Free did she think, when still within a few paces of her master? Swift as the wind she flew from the villa, in the direction of the river-side, scarce knowing which path she took in her eagerness to escape.

Her footsteps made no sound upon the dewy turf, and she did not hear another footstep hurrying close behind her.

A broad lawn stretched before her, and beyond that a thick plantation. Her anxiety was to reach this friendly shelter, for the moonlight night was bright and clear as day, and she trembled lest she should be perceived from the windows of the villa.

She was nearing the plantation when an iron hand was laid upon her shoulder, and turning round with a scream of mingled anguish and terror, she confronted Augustus Horton bare-headed in the moonlight. He had watched her escape from the window of his own apartment, and had lingered long enough to allow her to imagine herself free before he had left the house in pursuit of her.

"So, Cora," he said, "this is the way you repay me for my foolish indulgence. This is how you show your gratitude for being received at Hortonville like a princess! Do you know how we treat runaway slaves in the South?"

"No," answered Cora, with a look of defiance.

"Oh! you don't; I'm afraid they neglected your education in England."

"They did," replied the Octoroon; "the free citizens of that land of liberty forgot to teach me that beneath God's bounteous Heaven, there live a race of men who traffic in the bodies and souls of their fellow-creatures! That was a lesson they forgot to teach me."

"Then, I'm afraid you'll have to learn it here," said the planter; "and if you don't take care what you're about, it may be taught you in rather a rough fashion. But why, why, Cora, do you compel me to use this language? It is not the right of a master that I would exercise, but that of a lover."

"You forget," replied Cora, with icy coldness, "that I love, and am beloved by an honourable man, who would make me his wife."

"It is you who must forget that, Cora," answered Augustus, fiercely. "Henceforth, Gilbert Margrave and you are strangers. You are mine, I have kept my promise; I have given the fifty thousand dollars owed me by your father as the price of this moment. But it is not as a master that I address you. The rigours of slavery are not for you. Reward my devotion with one smile, one word of encouragement, and a life of luxury shall be yours; but, if you value your own happiness, do not force me to remember—"

"That I am your slave. Pardon me, Mr. Horton, it is that which I would not forget; but, as my English education has left me very ignorant, I must beg you to teach me the duties of a slave."

"Those duties are told in one word, Cora," replied the planter, "and that word is SUBMISSION! Absolute and unquestioning submission to every wish of the master. Blind obedience to every word, to each command, however revolting to the will of the slave. Body and soul, Cora, you are mine. Shriek, and your voice will echo through the plantation, but will awake no answer; for those who alone could hear it are slaves like yourself, and powerless to help you. Cease this mad folly then, and thus let me—"

He advanced as if to encircle her in his arms, but the Octoroon stepped back a few paces, and raising the cord which she held in her right hand, addressed him thus:–

"One step further, and it is I who will inflict upon you the chastisement of a slave, by striking you across the face."

As Cora uttered these words, a whistle resounded through the plantation, near the spot upon which she and the planter stood, and in another moment two dark figures emerged from the shade of the trees.

Before Augustus could interpose, Cora was seized in the arms of one of these men, and carried into the plantation, while the other grasped the shoulder of the planter with a hand of iron.

The moonlight on this man's face revealed his identity to Augustus.

"Gilbert Margrave!" he exclaimed.

"Aye, Gilbert Margrave, the affianced husband of the woman you would have destroyed. You refused to-day to accede to the appeal made by one gentleman to another. You gave me the answer of a *ruffian*; to-night it is I who use the ruffian's argument, *force!*"

"The law shall make you pay dearly for this," cried Augustus, hoarse with rage.

"Be it so. I am an Englishman, and am willing to suffer the worst penalty the laws of Louisiana can inflict upon me, rather than sacrifice the honour of my affianced wife."

The man who had seized Cora, disappeared beneath the shade of the trees. Gilbert tried to follow him, but Augustus Horton sprang towards him, with an open bowie knife in his hand.

"I am armed," cried Gilbert, "and wrong has made me desperate, follow me at your peril."

He bounded through the brushwood, and reached the bank of the river, by the side of which was moored a boat, with three men, who held their oars, ready to strike the water at the first signal. The man carrying Cora had already taken his place at the stern of the boat; Gilbert sprang in after them, the oars dipped into the water, and before Augustus Horton reached the brink of the river, the boat had shot out towards the centre of the stream.

Upon his own estate, and within a few hundred yards of a regiment of slaves, the planter had been defied and defeated in his hour of triumph.

The Octoroon had fainted from the excitement of the moment, but the cool breeze from the river quickly restored her to consciousness. When she re-opened her eyes, she found herself reclining on the shoulder of the man who had seized her.

That man was her father, Gerald Leslie.

CHAPTER XXIX.
THE MEETING OF THE LOVERS.

The two men whom Pauline Corsi had met on her way from the house of Silas Craig, to the Villa Moraquitos, are not entirely strangers to us.

We saw them last in the solitude of California, living a life of labour, far from all civilized society.

They only reached New Orleans upon the evening after the slave auction, and when Pauline Corsi met them, they were in search of an hotel where they could spend the night. In outward appearance they were very much altered from the day when we last beheld them. Their rough garments were exchanged for the fashionable attire of gentlemen, and their bearing harmonised well with the change in their costume.

Let us return to the moment when Pauline Corsi met these two gold diggers.

They entered the hotel, and were immediately conducted to a handsomely furnished, and brilliantly lighted apartment upon the first floor.

The elder of the two men, the one who called himself Smith, flung himself into an easy chair, after dismissing the waiter with an order for a couple of bottles of claret and Seltzer water, and looked complacently round the room.

The younger man walked to the open window, from which he watched the receding form of Pauline Corsi, who, after observing the two men enter the hotel, had hurried onward towards the end of the deserted street.

"This is a little better than the diggings, eh, Brown?" said Smith.

His companion seemed scarcely to hear him.

"That girl's figure reminds me—" he muttered, "but, pshaw! what foolish fancies have addled my brain! *She* is far away on the shores of another continent."

"What are you muttering about over there, man?" said Smith, who was evidently in very high spirits; "come here, and drink a tumbler of claret, and let's talk of our plans. To-night has brought us to the end of our journey. The time for silence is past, the hour has come in which we are to speak freely."

"It has."

"Remember; I ask your confidence from no spirit of idle curiosity, and, unless you can give it as freely as I shall give you mine, withhold it altogether."

Brown held out his hand, and grasped that of his companion.

"Friend, brother," he exclaimed, "there shall be no longer a secret between us. I will be the first to speak, light your cigar, and fill your glass, for the story I have to tell will be a long one."

* * * * * * *

It was past three o'clock, when the two men retired to rest; they had talked long and earnestly, and the reader will soon learn the purport of their conversation.

But late as they had sat up over night, the two friends breakfasted together early the next morning. They were too much excited to sleep long.

A New Orleans paper, published that morning, lay on the breakfast-table.

Smith opened the journal, and ran his eye hastily over its columns. It contained a full account of the slave auction of the previous day. The gold-digger's face blanched as he read the paragraph.

"Gracious Providence," he ejaculated, solemnly, "how mysterious are thy ways! I have but come in time. Cora, the beloved daughter of Gerald Leslie, sold in the public auction room! It is too horrible!"

He put on his hat, and after a few hasty words to his friend, hurried down stairs to the bar of the hotel, where he ordered a vehicle to be got ready for him, without delay.

It was strange, that, though so evidently anxious to depart, he preferred waiting for this vehicle, to walking through the sunny streets.

He had, no doubt, some powerful motive for this line of conduct.

In ten minutes, a close carriage was at the door, and, slouching his hat over his eyes, the gold-digger hurried from the bar to the vehicle, into which he sprang, after giving a brief direction to the negro driver.

Meanwhile, his companion lounged over his untasted breakfast. The New Orleans papers appeared to possess little interest for him. He looked at them for a few moments and then threw them carelessly aside.

He had shaved off the bushy whiskers which he had worn in the Californian solitude, and his face was only adorned by a small brown moustache.

He was about five-and-thirty years of age, but so slim and elegant in figure as to look considerably younger; and it was easy to see that he was not a native of America.

Half an hour after the departure of his friend, the waiter brought him a note which had been left at the hotel by an elderly mulattress.

At the first glance at the superscription on this note, the face of the man who called himself Brown, was convulsed by a tumult of emotion.

The letter was addressed to "Monsieur Armand Tremlay."

He tore asunder the envelope, and perused the few lines it contained, then snatching up his hat, he rushed from the house, to the alarm of the waiters, who were inclined to think the stranger had suddenly lost his senses.

A quarter of an hour afterwards, he was at the Villa Moraquitos.

It was now ten o'clock, and eleven had been appointed for the performance of the marriage ceremony, but neither the bride nor bridesmaid had as yet assumed the attire prepared for the occasion, and the elderly bridegroom, Don Juan Moraquitos, paced uneasily up and down his solitary chamber.

The gold-digger was admitted by the mulattress, Pepita. It was she who had carried the note to his hotel.

She conducted him to the elegant boudoir, usually occupied by Camillia Moraquitos and Pauline Corsi, but which was now untenanted.

The stranger gazed around him in bewilderment, but before he could ask a question of Pepita, she had hurried from the room.

He took the note from his waistcoat pocket, and once more devoured its brief contents.

"If Armand Tremlay would ascertain the fate of her whom he once loved, let him call without delay at the Villa Moraquitos."

He had read and re-read these words, during the brief interval he had to wait, before he heard a light footstep approaching the door of the room.

The door opened, and Pauline Corsi stood before him.

Another moment, and she was clasped in the stranger's arms.

"Pauline," he exclaimed, "my beloved, my darling, what magic is this? How is it, that after thirteen weary years I find you here in America?"

"Because I came hither to seek you, Armand! But tell me, before I say another word, have you been to France during the past thirteen years?"

"Seven years ago I was in Paris – seven years ago, I returned to my native country, wealthy and distinguished, to fling all at the feet of her, whom I dared to hope might still be faithful. A bitter blow awaited me on my arrival."

"Stay, Armand," said Pauline, laying her hand lightly upon her lover's lips; "tell me all, as it occurred from the first."

She pointed to a sofa and seated herself by the side of Armand Tremlay. Upon a table near her lay the bridal wreaths, which were to be worn by herself and Camillia. The Frenchman perceived the floral coronets, and asked eagerly,

"These orange blossoms, Pauline, for whom are they intended?"

"You shall know that by-and-bye," she answered, with an arch smile; "not another word, until I have heard your story."

An observer would have wondered at the transformation which the presence of Armand Tremlay effected in Pauline Corsi. She was no longer the cold and ambitious woman, but a loving and gentle girl, with the tender light of affection beaming in her blue eyes.

"Tell me," she repeated; "tell me all, Armand!"

"You remember the day upon which the Duke de B—— dismissed me from his house."

"Remember it," answered Pauline, "I have good reason to remember it. That day was the turning point of my life."

"And of mine. Reckless and desperate, I strode through the streets of Paris, with my breast rent with contending love and hatred. Love for you – hatred for the conventionalities of rank, which elevated an insurmountable barrier between genius and beauty; for I felt that I had genius, energy, and patience, to conquer fortune – all the gifts which help to make men great, and which the haughty lordling dare not despise, since they are at the root of all aristocracies. The very air of France seemed hateful to me, for I despised a country in which the differences of rank could part those whom Heaven had created for each other. I sailed for America, determined that in a free country I would attain such eminence as might entitle me to sue for the hand of a duke's daughter. So enraged was I against the fate which had separated us, that I threw aside my old name, and whatever small degree of distinction might be attached to it, and called myself Forester Townshend."

"And it was thus, that my search for you was fruitless," said Pauline; "but go on."

"Under that assumed name, I won considerable eminence as a portrait painter, throughout the United States, and seven years after leaving France, had amassed a considerable fortune. I returned to my native country, resolved, if I found you still true to me, to make one more appeal to the Duke; and failing in obtaining his consent, to persuade you to agree to a clandestine marriage. On reaching Paris, my first act was to go to the house you had occupied with your supposed father and mother. I was told that the family had removed to Milan. I lost not an hour in travelling to that city, and there I heard from the Duke's steward, the story of Jeannette's deathbed confession, and the heartless way in which you had been treated by those who for nearly seventeen years had caressed you as their only child."

"But they never loved me," murmured Pauline.

"No, dearest; it was an heir for a haughty title, and not a father's affections, that they sought. Providence punished their ambition, and terrible retribution overtook them for their cruelty in visiting upon your innocent head the crimes of others. The Duchess died, broken-hearted at the discovery of her guilty deception, and the Duke was stabbed by an assassin in the streets of Milan. It is thought that this assassin was his kinsman and the heir to his fortune."

Pauline bowed her head in silence.

"This story is very terrible," she said, solemnly; "I had long ago forgiven their wrong to me, in casting me from home and shelter; but I had never forgiven them for parting me from him I loved."

"Dearest Pauline, the ways of Providence are indeed inscrutable. I left Milan, after vainly endeavouring to ascertain whither you had gone after leaving the ducal palace. My enquiries were vain, and my only thought was to find you in Paris, to which city I imagined you would have fled. I remained in Paris for three months, during which time I inserted numerous advertisements in the papers, and applied to the police in order to discover your retreat. At the end of that time, I began to despair of ever finding you, and I was seized with a gloomy conviction that you had committed suicide in the first moments of your anguish. I left my fortune in the hands of my mother, in whose care it has been accumulating year by year, and withdrawing only sufficient to pay my voyage to America, I once more turned my back upon my native country."

"You returned to America."

"I did, but I was an altered man. I had no longer a purpose to uphold me – the motive for industry was gone. I travelled from city to city, earning plenty of money by my art, but spending it recklessly; and, forgive me, Pauline, wasting it often in the transient excitement of the gaming-table. I was too restless to remain in one place; I sought for change of scene, and for a life of action, for I was forever haunted by the memory of your unhappy fate; and one day I found myself in San Francisco, homeless and penniless. I had flung away my last dollar at the gaming-table. It was then that I resolved on accumulating a second fortune, and returning to France once more to seek for you. A sudden inspiration seemed to take possession of my mind; I felt that in all I had done, I had not done enough, and I determined to redouble my efforts, and devote the remainder of my life to the search for you."

"And you have succeeded."

"Aye, Pauline, in so unlooked for a manner, that I almost doubt now if this is not some strange but rapturous dream."

"You have arrived at New Orleans in time to assist at my wedding."

"Your wedding?"

"Yes, this day I become the wife of a wealthy Spaniard."

"Pauline!"

"Armand!" She held out her hand to him as she spoke, and in the expression of that one word, "Armand," there was enough to tell him that he had no cause for fear. He lifted the little hand to his lips and covered it with kisses.

He was interrupted by the entrance of the mulattress, Pepita, who brought a sealed packet addressed to Pauline Corsi, in the hand of Silas Craig.

Pauline took the packet, and glanced carelessly at the address.

"Has Mr. Lisimon arrived yet, Pepita?" she asked.

"He has, Mademoiselle; he is in the drawing-room."

"Very good, Pepita; and Donna Camillia, where is she?"

"In her own room, Mademoiselle."

The mulattress retired. Pauline broke the seals of the envelope, and took from it a parchment document, folded in an oblong form. Upon the flap of the envelope were written these words:–

"I send you that which you required of me. The advertisement appears in to-day's paper. – S.C."

"Come, Armand," said Pauline, "I have changed much since you first knew me; the bitter wrongs of my youth had a terrible influence upon my womanhood. I have been ambitious, heartless, mercenary, designing; but with your return my old nature comes back to me, and the fresh feelings of my girlhood revive."

"My dearest Pauline! but this marriage – that bridal wreath."

"Shall be worn by me, but not to-day. Tell me, Armand, do you still love me, the nameless orphan, the spurious child, as you did, when you thought me the heiress of one of Italy's proudest dukes? Have your feelings for me undergone no change since you learned that secret?"

"They have, Pauline, a very great change."

"Armand!"

"Yes, my beloved, and the change is that you are ten times dearer to me to-day, than you were ten years ago; for I have known what it is to lose you."

They descended to the drawing-room, where Paul Lisimon was seated in company with two of the most fashionable men in the city; guests who had been invited to witness the intended marriage ceremony.

Every citizen in New Orleans had seen the advertisement in that morning's paper, an advertisement which declared the entire innocence of Paul Lisimon of the crime imputed to him, and described the whole affair as a practical joke.

The young man rose as Pauline Corsi entered the room, and dropping his voice, said to her, "I received your letter from the hands of Captain Prendergills, and am here in answer to your summons."

"And you have seen the advertisement?"

"Yes; tell me in Heaven's name – how did you work so great a miracle?"

Pauline smiled with arch significance.

"When a woman has a powerful will, there is scarcely anything she cannot accomplish. When last we met, Paul Lisimon, I made you a proposal, which you rejected with scorn. In spite of my anger, I honoured you for that rejection; I am now about to avenge myself."

"How, Mademoiselle?"

"I no longer address you as Paul Lisimon; that name is in itself a lie; Paul Crivelli, read this document; it is the genuine will of your father, Don Tomaso."

As she spoke, she placed the parchment which had been sent her by Silas Craig, in the hands of the bewildered young man.

This brief dialogue had been spoken in so low a tone as to escape the ears of the two visitors standing by the chimney-piece. It was only overheard by Armand Tremlay, to whom the entire conversation was unintelligible.

At this moment a young mulattress entered the room, and announced "Captain Prendergills."

CHAPTER XXX.
THE SUPPRESSED DOCUMENT.

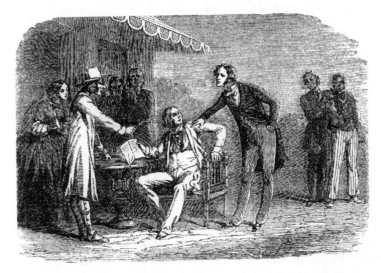

SILAS CRAIG'S DISMAY ON THE DISCOVERY OF THE SUPPRESSED DOCUMENTS

Augustus Horton left the plantation at daybreak on the morning after the scene between himself and Cora Leslie.

He knew that he had the law upon his side, and that Gilbert Margrave might be made to pay dearly for his abduction of the Octoroon.

But what if Gilbert and Cora should escape, and make their way to the Free States of America?

He was almost mad with fury as this thought arose to his brain. Immediately upon his arrival in New Orleans, he despatched a messenger for his confederate and evil counsellor, Silas Craig, and at nine o'clock the two men were seated opposite to each other at a well furnished breakfast table.

Augustus was terrified at beholding the change which the last twelve hours had wrought in the appearance of the attorney.

His face was almost ghastly in its corpse-like hue; purple circles surrounded his blood-shot eyes, and his lips were black and dry, like those of a sufferer in the worst stage of fever.

Throughout the weary night he had never ceased to pace up and down the narrow space in his office, pondering upon his interview with Pauline Corsi.

The whole scaffolding of his life had fallen away, leaving him well nigh crushed amongst the ruins.

The dark labyrinth of crime was closing upon his steps, and he knew not the end which lay before him.

But Augustus Horton was ignorant of the darker crimes which had left their foul stain upon the lawyer's life. He knew him to be an unscrupulous rogue, and associated with him because he was useful.

The first step taken by the two men was to communicate with the police, informing them of the abduction of Cora, and offering a large reward for the apprehension of the fugitives.

This done, Silas Craig told his employer of the advertisement which had been inserted in that day's paper, the advertisement which cleared the character of Paul Lisimon, and described the whole affair of the robbery as a practical joke.

The rage and mortification of Augustus knew no bounds. He declared that he had been fooled, duped, played with, by Silas Craig; and demanded what right the lawyer had to serve him in this manner.

"Scoundrel!" he said; "you have been bribed by Camillia Moraquitos; that Spanish woman has paid you to betray me."

"You have no need to call hard names, Mr. Horton," answered Silas; "I have been paid by no one. It was necessary to my own welfare to do this; and I have done it. Think yourself lucky that I did not betray you, and let the worthy citizens of New Orleans know your share in the transaction."

Augustus Horton's cheeks and brow flushed purple with suppressed rage. He felt that he was in the attorney's power; and that a word from Silas might blast his name forever.

"Come!" he said; "the business is done it seems; it is therefore too late to talk of it. My first task must be to find this Octoroon and her lover."

"True. Every moment is of value to us if we are not to let them escape."

"Escape!" cried Augustus, furiously; "I would sooner perish in the attempt to overtake them."

"Come, then! the Saint Louis packet starts in ten minutes from this time. They may take that opportunity of leaving the city."

The two men hurried to the quay; but they were too late; the steamer had started half an hour earlier than the time mentioned by Silas Craig.

They made enquiries of the clerks about the pier, but no one seemed able to give them any information.

As they were leaving the quay, Silas Craig uttered an exclamation of astonishment, on recognising the lanky figure of William Bowen, who was advancing towards them at a leisurely pace. The overseer wore a broad brimmed straw hat, and the light linen coat and trousers customary throughout Louisiana.

"You here, William!" exclaimed Silas, with surprise; "I thought you were at Iberville, where I left you in charge of my plantation."

Bowen laughed, and glanced with rather a peculiar expression at the attorney.

"I know you did," he said; "but you see I've left those parts. I guess I wrote you a letter, Mr. Craig, a week or two ago."

"You did."

"In which I asked you the loan of a thousand dollars?"

"Why, yes."

"And I guess you refused 'em?"

The attorney bit his lip, and glanced from Augustus to Bowen.

"Ah, I don't mind Mr. Horton knowing our private transactions," said Bill; "I asked for the loan of a paltry thousand dollars, and you refused me. Now, considering all these things, I thought this was rather shabby conduct, so I've discharged myself from your employment, and I calculate you'll have to look out for another overseer."

Augustus Horton was prepared to see the attorney resent the insolence of this speech, but to his surprise Silas seemed only anxious to conciliate Bowen.

"My dear William," he said, "you must remember that you have driven me rather hard lately. However, suppose you call upon me at my office. We'll settle matters there."

"We will settle matters, I reckon, Mr. Craig," answered Bowen, and a close observer might have detected a peculiar significance in his tone.

But Silas Craig was too much agitated to perceive this. He had not yet recovered from the extraordinary revealments made to him in his interview with Pauline Corsi. He felt like a man who walks blindfold upon the verge of a precipice, and who knows that every new footstep may hurl him to the gulf below.

Augustus and the attorney were leaving the quay when William Bowen called after them.

"I guess you were up to something down here, gents," he said; "you were looking after somebody, weren't you?"

"We were," answered Augustus; "we were in search of a runaway slave."

"The gal as you're after is Gerald Leslie's daughter, the Octoroon, I'll lay a hundred dollars," cried Bowen.

"She is."

The overseer laughed aloud–

"I'm darned if I didn't calculate as much," he said; "then I'm sorry to tell you, Mr. Horton, that the young lady's bolted with that Britisher as was so uncommon peart on board the Selma. They left by the Saint Louis packet half an hour ago. I thought there was something in the wind, but I'd no authority to stop 'em."

"D—n!" muttered Augustus Horton; "that Englishman has foiled me at every turn. The next packet for Saint Louis starts the day after to-morrow. They'll have eight and forty hours start of us, and they'll make their way to a Free State."

He walked away from the quay, followed by Silas Craig.

"If there's law in New Orleans," he cried, "I'll have them overtaken, and brought back."

William Bowen stood for some minutes, watching the two men as they walked away.

"I think I managed that job rather neatly," he said, with a malicious chuckle. "I've paid you out, Mr. Augustus Horton, for any impudence I've ever taken from you; and in a couple of hours more, my friend, Silas Craig, you and I will have squared our accounts for the last time."

Augustus and the attorney walked back to the house of the former, after making arrangements for the pursuit of Cora Leslie and her lover. The planter was maddened by his defeat, and utterly merciless to the unhappy girl who had, for a time at least, escaped from his power.

"I'll have her brought back," he cried, "and lashed as a runaway slave. I'll have her advertised in every paper in Louisiana. I'll spend every dollar I possess rather than let her escape me, and I'll make Gilbert Margrave pay dearly for his insolence."

Silas and the planter found Adelaide Horton and Mrs. Montresor seated beneath the verandah of the morning room, which opened into a small garden.

The weather was so warm, that the two ladies had left the interior of the apartment for the airy shade of this verandah. We have not seen Adelaide Horton since the scene on board the Selma – that disgraceful scene, in which the young girl had suffered the pangs of jealousy to goad her to an action unworthy of the better feelings of her impulsive nature. Bitter and immediate had been the punishment which followed that action. Despised by the man she had loved, cast off by her cousin and affianced husband, Mortimer Percy; harassed with the tortures of self-reproach, the unhappy girl had ample cause for painful reflection and regret. She would have made any sacrifice to recall her words of denunciation the moment after their utterance.

The memory of her old friendship for Cora Leslie stung her to the heart, and the mildly reproachful gaze of the Octoroon haunted her perpetually.

Mrs. Montresor had done her best to console her niece; but Adelaide's gaiety and light heartedness had entirely deserted her. She was no longer the same high-spirited girl who had arrived two months before in New Orleans.

The ladies looked up from their work as Augustus and the lawyer approached them. Adelaide perceived her brother's ill-concealed agitation, and asked the cause of it.

He related his adventure on the quay.

"Then Cora and Gilbert Margrave have left for Saint Louis?"

"They have," answered Augustus with an oath, "but they shall not long escape me. Listen to me, Adelaide; you may wonder at the passion I feel upon this subject, but my pride has been humiliated by the cool insolence of the Octoroon, and whatever motive I may have had for my conduct at the slave-sale yesterday, I have now no purpose but that of bringing Cora Leslie's haughty spirit to the dust. I will have her found and brought back to New Orleans, and I will give her to you as your lady's-maid. I know that there is little love lost between you, and that I could not easily inflict a greater humiliation upon my fine lady."

"And you will give her to me?" exclaimed Adelaide with evident delight.

"Yes. I thought you'd like the idea."

"You will give me Cora Leslie?"

"I will. The girl cost me fifty thousand dollars, but I care for nothing now but revenge. Make her your lady's-maid – bring her nose to the grindstone – let her feel what it is to be the slave of the woman who hates her."

"I will gladly accept your gift, Augustus," said Adelaide, eagerly; "but I fear that you will change your mind."

"No, indeed!"

"Then suppose you write a memorandum of your gift, and sign it in the presence of Mr. Craig and my aunt."

"Willingly," replied Augustus, and seating himself at the table he scrawled a few lines, transferring the Octoroon to his sister, and after signing the document, pushed it across to Silas Craig.

"Witness that, Craig," he said, "since my sister is so much afraid of my breaking my word."

Adelaide took up the paper, glanced at its contents, and placed it in the pocket of her dress.

"I cannot tell you, my dear Augustus, how grateful I am to you for this gift," she said, exchanging a look of peculiar significance with her aunt, Mrs. Montresor.

Five minutes afterwards, Myra, the Quadroon slave, announced Mr. Leslie and Mr. Percy.

Augustus Horton started at the sound of those names. Mortimer Percy had been absent from New Orleans since the night of the duel between his cousin and Gilbert Margrave. A faint flush suffused the cheek of Adelaide Horton; she felt that she was about to meet the man who had once loved, but now despised her.

Augustus was utterly ignorant that Gerald Leslie had assisted in carrying off the Octoroon; he had recognised no one but Gilbert Margrave, upon the night of the abduction.

The planter received his visitors with cold politeness, but the rat-like eyes of the attorney glanced with a look of hatred at Gerald Leslie.

Mr. Leslie was not alone, Toby, the mulatto, followed him into the garden.

Silas Craig started from his seat with an angry oath. "What brings you here," he cried to Toby.

"Do not blame him, Mr. Craig," answered Gerald Leslie, quietly, "it is I who brought Toby here."

"Oh, it was you, was it? and by what right do you order my slaves about, pray, Mr. Leslie?"

"You will learn that in due time; I have reason to think that Toby's presence will be needed."

The attorney quailed beneath the steady gaze of Gerald Leslie. He felt that some hidden danger was threatened by this visit.

"Pray, Mr. Leslie," said Augustus Horton, "may I venture to ask the motive which has brought you and my cousin to a house in which you can hardly expect to be welcome?"

"You will very soon know that, Mr. Horton," answered Gerald. "Our visit to-day is to Mr. Craig, rather than to yourself; and our motive in coming to this house is that you may learn the true character of the man whom you have chosen as your associate."

"I require no such teaching, Mr. Leslie," said Augustus, haughtily. "Silas Craig, why do you sit there like a stock? Why don't you speak, man; and ask Gerald Leslie what he means by this?"

"Shall I answer that question, Mr. Horton," replied Leslie. "Silas Craig does not speak because he dares not; because he knows his own guilt, and knows that the seizure and sale of my property, which took place yesterday, was an illegal one."

"Illegal?"

"Yes, illegal; because that seizure was made for a debt which I did not owe. The sole claim which that man, Silas Craig, had upon me, was a debt of one hundred thousand dollars. That debt was paid to him a year ago by my late partner, Philip Treverton."

Silas Craig laughed aloud; but it was a hollow and affected mirth, which could scarcely have deceived the most shallow observer.

"You are either a fool or a madman, Gerald Leslie," he said. "If Philip Treverton had paid the money he would have had a receipt for it from me. In the absence of such a document, who can prove the payment of the debt?"

"I can!" exclaimed William Bowen, emerging from the window of the morning room. "You refused me a paltry thousand dollars, Mr. Silas Craig; I reckon I've paid you out for your shabby conduct. Here's the receipt – the genuine document – in your own handwriting, signed with your own name, and given by you to Philip Treverton."

He thrust an open paper into the attorney's hand. Silas sat gasping at the document, as if he had been rooted to the spot.

"Aye, you may stare," said Bowen. "You told me to burn that paper, didn't you, upon the night of Philip Treverton's death? And you saw me burn it as you thought; but I knew the slippery customer I had to deal with, and I changed the papers. You thought you heard footsteps outside the door, and while you turned round to listen I substituted a blank sheet of foolscap for the receipt, and thrust it into the fire. You saw the blaze, and you were satisfied. I kept the genuine document, thinking it might be useful."

CHAPTER XXXI.
THE FOOTSTEPS OF THE AVENGER.

STRUGGLE BETWEEN PAUL AND TRISTAN

Paul Lisimon received the parchment from the hand of Pauline Corsi, with the bewildered manner of one who scarce knows whether he is awake or dreaming; but the entrance of the Captain of the Amazon obliged the young man to recover from the temporary stupor into which he had been thrown.

"Mademoiselle Corsi?" he exclaimed; "Prendergills, what does this mean?"

"It means," answered the Frenchwoman, "that you should guard that paper as dearly as your life. Ask me no questions till you have seen Don Juan Moraquitos, and come with me at once to his study. Captain Prendergills, you will wait until I summon you?"

"Yes, Mademoiselle," answered the stalwart sailor.

"You, Armand, will leave me for to-day," murmured Pauline, placing her hand in that of her lover; "I have a task to perform before I shall be worthy of your affection. In the meantime trust me, and wait."

"I will," answered the artist; "I will return to my hotel and be ready to attend you at any moment you may need my presence."

"Gentlemen," said the Frenchwoman, turning to the two visitors, who were looking on with considerable wonderment, at a scene they had been unable to comprehend; "I fear that we have sadly wasted your valuable time. Events have occurred which will unavoidably postpone the ceremony you were invited to witness."

"Then there will be no wedding to-day, Mademoiselle?"

"There will not."

"Don Juan is ill, I fear?" said one of the guests.

"He is not quite himself," answered Pauline, gravely.

The two gentlemen expressed their regret and retired, accompanied by Armand Tremlay. Captain Prendergills seated himself in an easy chair, and stretching his great legs upon an embroidered cushion, took a pipe and tobacco-pouch from his pocket, and prepared to enjoy himself.

"If you could send me a bottle of brandy to wet my lips with, while I'm waiting, I should take it kindly, Mademoiselle," he said.

Pauline promised that his request should be attended to, and left the room followed by Paul.

But on the threshold of Don Juan's private apartment, she paused and hesitated for a moment.

"He knows nothing yet of what has happened," she said; "I had better see him alone. Wait!"

She entered the apartment, and remained about a quarter of an hour. That period seemed an age to the young man as he paced up and down the hall.

He had thrust the parchment into the bosom of his coat. He was dying to peruse its contents, but refrained from doing so until he could gain the solitude of his own chamber.

He did not perceive two glaring eyes which followed his every movement from a dark corner of the shady hall.

The eyes were those of Tristan the slave, who stood concealed behind one of the pillars which supported the ceiling of the apartment. Pauline Corsi at last emerged from the chamber of Don Juan.

"He will not see you yet," she said; "but in two hours from this time you are to go to him, and all will be arranged. He promises that the past shall be atoned for, at least as far as you are concerned. In the meantime you had better rest, for you look haggard and worn out, as if you had not slept for long."

"I have not," answered Paul; "my duties on board the Amazon and my own troubles have both hindered me from sleep."

"Then go to your own room and rest. Remember your interview with Don Juan will be a painful one, and you will need to be prepared for it."

"But Camillia, let me see her—"

"Not until you have seen her father. Nay, do not think me cruel; trust me, I act for the best. She has seen your name and character cleared to the eyes of the world, and she is happy. You will forget the foolish words I spoke to you when last we met in the house, and you will trust me, will you not?"

"I will, Pauline."

"Then prove your trust by implicit obedience."

"I will," answered the young man.

He retired to his old apartment. It had been undisturbed since the day on which he quitted it. His books and papers all remained as he had left them, but not a speck of dust had gathered upon any article in the room.

He knew not that this was owing to the orders given by Camillia Moraquitos to her favourite slave, Pepita.

He entered the chamber, and was about to secure the door before reading the document given to him by Pauline, but he found, to his surprise, that there was no key in the lock.

He had always been in the habit of locking the door, and he knew, therefore, that the key had been removed since he left the villa.

Taking the parchment from his breast he seated himself near the window, beneath the shade of the Venetian shutters, and commenced his examination of the all-important document. It was the last will and testament of Tomaso Crivelli, in which the Spaniard bequeathed his entire fortune to his only and beloved son, Paul Crivelli. Attached to the will was a letter addressed to Paul, in which Don Tomaso revealed to him that he was the son of a favourite Quadroon slave, whom the Spaniard had married after giving her her freedom. The marriage had been kept a secret on account of the false pride of Don Tomaso, which would not permit him to acknowledge as his wife one who was known to have been a slave.

After reading these two documents the young man fell upon his knees in an attitude of thanksgiving.

"Providence, I thank thee!" he exclaimed; "I am no longer a nameless outcast – a dependent on the charity of strangers. He whom I so dearly loved was indeed my father, and humble though my mother may have been, her son has no cause to blush for her."

His next care was to place the precious documents in safety. He would not trust them about his own person lest his uncle should have found some plot to get them from him; he therefore secured them in a small leathern portmanteau, the lock of which would have defied the cleverest thief in America. The key he attached to a thin gold chain, which he wore under his waistcoat, and which held the locket containing Camillia's portrait; the locket which had been observed by Augustus Horton. Having done this Paul looked at his watch. The whole business had only occupied half an hour; he had therefore an hour and a half to wait before his interview with Don Juan Moraquitos.

Pauline Corsi had forbidden him to leave his apartments until summoned to that interview.

He took up a book, but was unable to concentrate his attention upon the pages.

A low couch stood near the open window, and Paul threw himself upon the cushions, and abandoned himself to reflection. He did not mean to sleep, but the morning was hot and sultry; and exhausted by excitement and by long nights of fatigue, his eyes closed and he fell into a slumber.

While he lay in that strange state of semi-consciousness, which is neither sleeping nor waking, he fancied that he saw a dark figure glide softly in at the door of the chamber and conceal itself behind the ample folds of the window curtains.

This figure entered the room with so noiseless a tread, and disappeared so quickly that Paul, whose eyes had been closed all the time, thought the apparition formed part of his dream.

He fell into a deep slumber, from which he was suddenly aroused by the shutting of the door of his apartment.

This door had been closed so quietly, that the sound would have been unheard by an ordinary sleeper; but the over-strained state of the young man's nerves was such that a whisper would have awakened him.

The room was darkened by the closed Venetian shutters, which excluded the burning sun, and left the apartment in shadow. Paul sprang to his feet, and looked about him. The chamber was empty. He tore aside the window curtains, but there was no one lurking behind their voluminous draperies.

His next impulse was to look to the safety of the portmanteau. It was gone!

He had placed it on a chair near the couch, on which he lay, but the chair was empty.

He searched the apartment, but in vain; the portmanteau had disappeared.

He rushed from the room, and to the hall below; the first person he met was Pepita. He enquired of her, if she had met any one carrying a portmanteau.

"A little leather bag, massa?"

"Yes, yes."

"Tristan jes carry one out of de house den, massa; Pepita see him," answered the mulattress.

"Which way did he go?" exclaimed Paul, breathless with agitation.

"Out o' door, Massa Paul; to de wood-house, Pepita tink."

Paul waited to hear no more, but rushed to the back premises, amongst which the wood-house was situated.

The wood-house was a rudely constructed building, in which timber was kept for the stoves. As Paul approached the door, he perceived wreaths of pale blue smoke issuing from the crevices in the wood work.

This smoke indicated the burning of timber within the hut. Paul tried to open the door, but it was bolted on the inside. He flung himself with all his force against it, but it resisted his efforts.

He felt that the slave Tristan had taken the portmanteau into the hut for some evil design.

"Tristan!" he cried, "Tristan! open the door, or I will shoot you through a crevice in the wood."

The negro only answered with a mocking laugh. Meanwhile the smoke, increasing every minute in volume, almost suffocated the young man with its stifling fumes.

Suddenly Paul remembered that on the other side of the wood-house there was a small window which admitted light into the building.

He ran round to the window. The shutters were nailed together, but the wood was rotten and the hinges worn and rusty. Paul wrenched them asunder with the rapidity of lightning, dashed his hand through the dingy glass of the window, flung it open and sprang into the hut.

A log fire was blazing in the centre of the building, and Tristan the negro knelt over the flames with the portmanteau in his hand.

Paul sprang upon him and tore the leather case from his grasp, but the negro was the stronger of the two. He regained possession of the portmanteau and made towards the door of the hut. Again Paul flung himself upon him, and this time the struggle between the two men was terrible in its intensity. The face of Paul was white with concentrated rage, while the dilated eyes of the negro glared like those of a fiend.

Tristan's superior strength had nearly mastered his opponent, when, with a desperate effort, Paul grasped the portmanteau, and with one well planted blow, brought the negro to the ground.

He lay where he had fallen, stunned and motionless.

Paul returned to the house carrying the precious burden with him. Two hours had nearly expired, and the time approached for his interview with Don Juan.

He carried the portmanteau to his apartment, unlocked it, took out the documents and placed them once more in his bosom, determined to carry them on his person at any risk.

"They must kill me before they obtain them," he muttered.

He looked at his watch. The two hours had fully expired. The interview was to take place at one o'clock. The hands upon the dial pointed to the hour.

He left his room in order to proceed to Don Juan's apartment; but upon the landing-place his steps were arrested by a strange and appalling sound.

That sound was the report of a pistol which reverberated through the hall below.

Paul was not the only person who heard the ominous sound. As he paused for a moment, motionless with horror and alarm, the door of the apartment opposite to him was opened and Pauline Corsi stood upon the threshold.

She was not alone; close behind her appeared the pale face of Camillia Moraquitos.

Both the women were terribly agitated.

The Spanish girl endeavoured to rush out upon the landing, but Pauline threw her arms about her and arrested her steps.

"Keep her back," she cried; "if you love her, keep her back, Paul, while I go and see what that sound means."

Paul obeyed; he led Camillia back into her own apartment, and endeavoured to calm her agitation.

But in vain. She would not listen to his attempts at consolation; but implored him again and again to let her go to her father.

"I know that something dreadful has happened," she said; "you are all in league to deceive me. My father is in danger, and you are cruel enough to keep me from rushing to his side."

At this moment Pauline Corsi returned. The young man saw by her ghastly face that something terrible had indeed occurred.

"Come with me, Paul," she said; "you can see Don Juan now."

Camillia caught hold of her hand. "He can see my father. Ah, then, he is safe; he is safe, Pauline," she cried.

The Frenchwoman did not answer, but silently led Paul from the room.

He followed her down the stairs; but on the threshold of Don Juan's chamber she paused, and took the young man's hand in hers, which was icy cold.

"Prepare yourself for a fearful shock, Paul," she said, "and for an awful sight. Are you brave enough to encounter them?"

"What you, a woman, can endure, I can also bear," he answered calmly.

"Crime brings a fearful retribution," murmured the Frenchwoman, in an awe-stricken voice; "and however slow the footsteps of the avenger, he is not the less sure to overtake his victim. Your uncle has paid the penalty of his sins."

She opened the door, and the young man followed her into the chamber.

It was the chamber of death.

Don Juan Moraquitos lay upon the rich Persian carpet, his face towards the ground, and a pistol lying a few paces from his outstretched hand.

A more ghastly sight had never been shone upon by the bright summer sun, whose beams stole into the apartment through the Venetian shutters, and illuminated the blood-stained floor, on which the suicide was stretched.

Upon the table in the centre of the room, lay a letter addressed to Paul Crivelli.

The ink of the superscription was still wet, though the hand which had fashioned the characters was now that of a corpse. Paul tore open the envelope, and read the words written within. The suicide's letter ran thus:–

"You have been told a secret, which my guilt has kept from you for thirteen years. I do not ask you to forgive me, for you know not, and you will never know, what you have to forgive; I go to seek mercy from a higher tribunal than those which meet on earth. I could not live to blush beneath the glance of my nephew. You love my poor Camillia: make her happy, and the spirit of him who has wronged you will bless you even in death. She will be as rich as yourself. If your love for the daughter can ever prompt you to think with less anger of the father's guilt, you will be showing mercy to the unhappy wretch who writes these lines.

"Juan Moraquitos."

CHAPTER XXXII.
THE DEAD RETURNED TO LIFE.

Let us return to the moment at which Silas Craig received from the hands of William Bowen, his accomplice and tool, the document which he had fully believed to be destroyed.

It is thus that the wicked are always deserted and betrayed by their allies. The old phrase, "Honour among thieves," is a false and delusive one.

Among the dishonest there can be no honour. The same impulse which prompts them to cheat and deceive their victims, will, at another time, induce them to cheat each other.

Thus it was with the unscrupulous overseer, William Bowen; so long as his employer had paid him for his silence, he was content to suppress the guilty secret of the money which Silas had received from Philip Treverton, but on the first occasion of the attorney's refusing to supply him with funds, he was ready to turn round and betray him.

It was with this view that he had contrived to substitute a blank sheet of paper, and to preserve the actual receipt written and signed by Silas Craig.

The wealthy attorney, the pretended Christian, stood convicted a cheat and a swindler.

Augustus Horton turned indignantly from his old ally.

"Bear witness, Mr. Leslie, and you, Mortimer," he said, "that I did not know what this man was."

Silas Craig gnashed his teeth in silence; then crushing the paper in his hand, he rose from his chair and looked about him.

It was the look of a wild beast at bay; the look of a fox that knows the chase is over and the dogs are round him. He sees their glaring eyes, he feels their hot and hungry breath, but he determines on concentrating the energy of his nature on one last effort.

"This receipt is a forgery!" he screamed, in a shrill and broken voice. "I deny its validity!"

"Take care, Silas Craig," said his old accomplice, "I calculate lying won't save you. You'd better speak the truth for once in a way, I reckon, and throw yourself upon the mercy of these gents."

"I deny its validity!" repeated the attorney; "it's an infamous forgery, fabricated by that man, William Bowen. I defy any living creature to prove that Philip Treverton paid me one hundred thousand dollars."

"Beware, Silas Craig!" said a voice from the interior of the apartment. "You defy the living, do you also defy the dead?"

A man emerged from the shadow of the curtains about the window. That man was the elder of the two gold diggers; but he was no stranger to those assembled there.

"The dead!" gasped Silas, dropping once more into his chair.

Those present never forgot the expression of the attorney's face, as with open mouth and protruding eye-balls, he stared at the newcomer.

It was but for a moment that they beheld the gaze of horror, for after one brief glance he covered his face with his outspread hands.

"The dead!" he repeated; "the dead!"

"Philip Treverton!" exclaimed Gerald Leslie.

"Yes, Gerald," answered the stranger, extending his hand to Cora's father; "that Philip Treverton whom you have been taught to think a gamester and a cheat. That Philip to whom, when about to sail for England, you entrusted a large sum of money, to be paid by him to that wretch yonder. You departed, secure in the belief that your friend and partner was a man of honour, and that the money was as safe in his hands as in your own. On your return you were told that your friend was dead, and that the money had not been paid. I have only learned to-day, from the lips of Bowen there, your noble and generous conduct. You uttered no word of complaint, no syllable of reproach, but you bore up to the last against the reverses brought upon you, as you thought, by the dishonour of another."

"Do not speak of that, Philip," said Gerald Leslie; "I attributed the loss of the money to some fatal moment of imprudence, and I never, even in thought, accused you of dishonour."

"Imprudence would have been dishonour in such a case," answered Philip Treverton. "Ay, Silas Craig, well may you hide your face from me – well may your eyes refuse to meet those of the man you would have murdered!"

"Murdered!" exclaimed Gerald and Mortimer, while the women listened with white and terrified faces to the disclosures of the returned wanderer.

"Yes, murdered. It is a foul word to speak beneath the broad blue sky, and in the sunlight of yonder heaven, but it is the word for all that."

"Silas Craig," cried Augustus Horton, "have you no word to answer to all this? Can you sit calmly there and hear these accusations? Speak, man, speak, and give your accuser the lie."

"He cannot!" said Philip Treverton, pointing to the lawyer. "Is that the attitude of a man who is falsely accused? Look at him; look at him crouching like a beaten hound beneath its master's whip."

"Do not speak of him," cried Gerald Leslie, impetuously, "but explain this mystery. How is it that for a twelvemonth you have disappeared from New Orleans, to return at this moment of ruin and despair?"

"I will tell you," answered Philip Treverton; "and I call upon this man, William Bowen, here, to bear witness of my truth, and on yonder wretch to contradict me if he dare. Upwards of a year ago I was left by you with the sum of one hundred thousand dollars in my hands – the amount of the loan advanced to our firm by the usurer, Silas Craig. This was to be repaid upon a certain date; that date fell about a month after your departure for England. I held the money more sacred than my life, and I laid it by in the strong box devoted to important documents."

"You did as I myself would have done," said Gerald Leslie.

"I did; but I was by no means faultless. I was the victim of a vice which has brought dishonour upon men who never thought to blush before their fellow men – I was a gamester! I devoted my days to business cheerfully, conscientiously; but at night the demon of the dice-box lured me from my quiet home, and led me to a secret gaming-house in Columbia Street – a house known to all the gamblers of New Orleans, but which flourishes in bold defiance of the law. I had known this house for years, and had been a constant guest at its unholy altars, but there was one thing concerning it that I did not know."

"And that was—?"

"Its owner! I did not know that Silas Craig, the lawyer, the sanctimonious attorney whom men met every Sunday morning in the sacred temple of Heaven; I did not know that this man was the proprietor of that earthly hell, the wretch who pandered in secret to the vices of his fellow-citizens. I did not know this, and I did not know that the gaming-house in Columbia Street communicated by a secret passage with the office of Silas Craig."

"Impossible!" exclaimed Augustus Horton.

"Aye, the secret has been well kept; and it was a secret that was only to have been known to me when the hand of Death was on my lips to seal them to eternal silence. But the ways of Providence are inscrutable. The day arrived upon which our debt to this man became due. At twelve o'clock on that day I called, delivered to him the sum of one hundred thousand dollars in bills of exchange, and received his written acknowledgement of the money. This done I felt as light as a feather. A load was removed from my mind, and I determined to spend a day of enjoyment. I dined with some friends at an hotel, and after sitting late over the table, and drinking a good deal of wine, we adjourned to the gaming-house in Columbia Street."

There was a brief pause; but Silas Craig never stirred from his abject attitude, never attempted, by either word or gesture, to contradict the speaker.

"We played for some hours, but my friends were not such inveterate gamesters as myself, and they grew weary of the demoniac fever. After persuading me to quit the place with them, they at last lost patience with my folly and departed, leaving me still at the fatal green cloth. It was by this time four o'clock in the morning. I had drunk a great deal, and I had been losing money. My head was bewildered; my brain dizzy, and my temper soured by my losses. The room was almost deserted, but I still sat with my eyes fixed upon the game, madly endeavouring to retrieve my losses. At this crisis a great brawny fellow opposite to me, a Frenchman, ventured to insult me. Tipsy as I was, I was in no humour to brook this. I sprang towards him to chastise his insolence, and a fight ensued, in which I was getting the worst of it, when one of the bystanders interfered, and suggested that we should resort to small swords, and finish the business in a more gentlemanly manner."

"It was a plot!" said Gerald Leslie.

"It was! A villainous and foul plot, concocted by yonder stricken wretch. Stupefied and bewildered, I let them do what they pleased with me, and I know nothing of what happened till I found a duelling sword in my hand, and saw that my adversary was armed in the same fashion. By this time the room was entirely deserted, except by my antagonist, the other man, and myself. This other man – the same who had suggested our using swords – opened a door in the wall, a door which I had never before perceived, and pushed me into a long dimly lighted corridor, which was also strange to me. The door closed behind us, and we hurried along the corridor for some distance, until we were stopped by the stranger who had taken upon himself the management of the business. He placed us opposite to each other, put the swords into our hands, and gave us the signal to begin. I felt in a moment that I was a lost man. My head spun round. In the dim light I could scarcely see my adversary's face, as the lamps were so arranged that what light there was fell full upon mine. In vain I tried to parry his thrusts. I had been twice wounded slightly on the shoulder, when the lights were suddenly extinguished, and I felt the sharp pang of a stab from a long and slender sword.

"But this stab did not come from my opponent. Although I lost consciousness upon the moment of receiving the stroke, I knew that I was stabbed in the back."

"Execrable traitors!" exclaimed Gerald, Mortimer, and Augustus.

"When I recovered my senses I found myself in a lonely boat-house on the banks of the Mississippi, four miles from New Orleans. I was lying on a mattress, and my wound had been dressed by a surgeon; but I was too feeble, from loss of blood and the pain I had endured, to utter a word, or ask one question of the man seated by my side."

"You were not alone, then?"

"No! William Bowen, the accomplice of Silas Craig, had repented of the horrible work as soon as it was done; and, under pretence of carrying my body to the river, had contrived to convey me to this lonely shed, which belonged to a friend of his."

"Stop a bit, Mr. Treverton," interrupted William; "when Mr. Craig settled with me that we were to set that villainous Frenchman on to you, get up a duel, and rob you of the receipt for the hundred thousand dollars, it was agreed that you were to be attacked in fair fight, and that you were not to be seriously hurt. It was Mr. Silas Craig yonder who couldn't be content with this; it was he who turned out the gas in the thick of the fight, and stabbed you in the back. You dropped down like a dead man; but the lawyer there was too great a coward to make sure whether you were really dead; he dared not approach within a couple of yards of his victim. He told me to ransack your pockets, and secure the receipt; and then, assisted by the Frenchman, to carry the body to the river."

"And you did so?"

"I did; but I contrived to get rid of the Frenchman as soon as we reached the quay, and then, dropping my bleeding burden into a boat, I rowed down to the boat-house, where I sought a surgeon to look at my patient. Mr. Treverton knows the rest."

"I do, William," answered Philip Treverton; "I know that you attended me faithfully and patiently; and that when I recovered, you assisted me to get off to California, whence, after nearly a twelvemonths' toil, I return so rich a man as to be able to recompense the noble conduct of my old friend, Gerald Leslie. As for yonder wretch," he added, pointing to Craig, "defeat has followed so utterly upon his career of crime that I doubt if the law can do much more to punish him. He will refund the hundred thousand dollars of which he has defrauded his victim."

"I will," gasped the unhappy wretch, rising, and staggering towards the door; "I am rich; take what you will. I shall leave New Orleans forever—."

He stopped suddenly, and passed his handkerchief across his lips; when he removed it, it was stained with patches of crimson.

He had broken a blood-vessel!

CHAPTER XXXIII.
TRISTAN.

TRISTAN, THE NEGRO

A deathly and terrible gloom reigned in the Villa Moraquitos after the awful catastrophe which had closed the life of Don Juan.

It was impossible to keep the entire truth from Camillia. She was told that she was fatherless, but that the report which she had heard was the result of an accident. The poor girl was made to believe that Don Juan had perished through an accident which had occurred to him while cleaning the fire-arms that ornamented his study. Pauline Corsi watched over her with the tenderness of an elder sister; but the stricken girl abandoned herself to a grief which seemed almost inconsolable.

Late in the afternoon, Paul Crivelli left the house of death, and proceeded to the hotel at which Armand Tremlay was staying.

He was the bearer of a letter from Pauline Corsi; and he informed the artist of the terrible event which had happened since that morning.

"It will be, therefore, some months before I can hope that my cousin Camillia will assume the right to a still dearer name," said Paul, after they had talked for some time of the awful event.

"I imagine so," answered Armand; "and Pauline tells me that I must be patient, as she will not consent to our marriage taking place on any day but that appointed for yours."

The two young men left the hotel and walked through the more retired streets, until they left the city behind them, and emerged upon the banks of the river.

Armand Tremlay and Paul Crivelli were eminently suited to each other. So much, too, had the terrible event of the day broken down the barriers of ceremony and restraint, that they seemed already like old friends.

They walked on, talking of the singular occurrences which had checkered their two lives, until the sun was sinking into the bosom of the Mississippi, and until they found themselves at a considerable distance from the city.

In order to regain New Orleans by a shorter route, they struck into a wood that bordered the river.

The sun was fading behind the trunks of the trees, and the wood was lonely as some primeval forest.

They had walked for some little distance, when they came suddenly upon the figure of a negro, reclining at the foot of an immense American oak.

He started to his feet as they approached, and Paul recognised the man with whom he had that morning struggled, Tristan, the slave belonging to the late Don Juan.

The negro glared at him with a savage expression in his distended eyeballs.

"It is you," he cried, "you – you! You haunt me wherever I go. I had come here to die."

"To die?"

"Yes. I have poison here," he said, clutching at some object in the breast of his shirt. "I overheard all this morning, and I should have been your ruin, had you not overpowered me. I would have burnt the evidence of your birth. I would have prevented your union with Camillia Moraquitos – with her I love!"

"You are mad, Tristan."

"Yes, I am mad. What can that slave be but mad who dares to love his mistress? I would grovel upon the earth, and suffer her foot to trample upon my neck. I would die a thousand deaths, but I am mad, and I love her. I have loved her from those happy hours when she was a little child by yonder sunny river, and I was her plaything, her dog, her slave, but still her companion; and now she loathes and despises the wretched slave, and loves another, and mad Tristan has come into this forest to die."

The glaring eyes of the negro had so much of the fire of insanity in their savage light, that the two young men thought he was indeed mad.

"Tristan, Tristan!" said Paul, imploringly.

"Beware," cried the slave, snatching a knife from his breast. "Beware how you cross my path! You are unarmed, and strong as you are, feeble against the strength of madness. Avoid me, if you value your own safety; you, Paul Crivelli, above all others, should shun me, for I hate you. Avoid me then, if you would not tempt me to destroy you."

He uttered a wild cry, and sprang towards Paul, with the knife uplifted in his powerful right hand, but the two young men were prepared for the blow, and while Armand Tremlay seized the hand holding the dagger, Paul twisted a silk handkerchief into a bandage, with which they bound the arms of the negro.

Secured thus, they conveyed him back to New Orleans. The violent paroxysm of madness had passed, and the wretched man was as quiet as a child. They took him to the Villa Moraquitos, where they placed him under the care of his mother, assisted by a powerful negro, belonging to the household.

"Restore him to reason, Zara," said Paul, "and as soon as he has recovered, I will give you both your liberty."

"Good, generous massa, and we shall go back to Africa?"

"You shall."

CHAPTER XXXIV.
FAREWELL TO LOUISIANA.

CORA AND GILBERT AT THE GRAVE OF FRANCILIA

Gerald Leslie, William Bowen, and Philip Treverton accompanied Silas Craig to the attorney's office, where the wretched man refunded the hundred thousand dollars, and wrote a long and detailed confession of his guilt, which he signed in the presence of three witnesses.

This done, Gerald and his partner returned to the house of Augustus Horton, where they had left Mortimer Percy.

They found Augustus, Adelaide, and Mrs. Montresor seated in a brilliantly lighted apartment, communicating with the morning room that opened upon the garden.

Mortimer Percy was seated a little distance from his cousin, and it was evident that no reconciliation had taken place between them.

Adelaide and Mrs. Montresor were both engaged in some elegant needlework, which afforded them an excellent excuse for silence. Augustus stood near the open window smoking his cigar in moody stillness.

It was thus the group was occupied when Gerald Leslie and Philip Treverton returned from the lawyer's house.

Gerald was the first to speak–

"You will be surprised, perhaps, to see me again, Mr. Horton?" he said to Augustus.

"I will freely own that I am so," answered the planter; "though the conduct of my cousin, Mr. Percy, has made me accustomed to surprises.

The revelations of this morning have nothing to do with me, and I cannot imagine what can have brought Mr. Leslie and Mr. Treverton to this house."

Gerald Leslie smiled.

"Indeed, Mr. Horton! You forget, then, that I have a daughter?"

"I do not," answered Augustus. "I have very good reason to remember that fact, Mr. Leslie. The purchase of the Octoroon slave, Cora, cost me fifty thousand dollars, and there appears considerable chance of my losing every cent."

"Not if you can recapture your runaway slave," said Gerald Leslie.

"Not if I can recapture her. No, let her once fall into my hands, and it shall be my fault if she escapes again. As for the Englishman, Gilbert Margrave—"

"You will have no mercy upon him?" asked Gerald.

"By Heaven I will not. We Southerners are in no humour just now to put up with any of your abolitionist tricks, and Mr. Margrave shall pay dearly for breaking the laws of Louisiana."

Augustus walked up and down the room as he spoke, and every accent revealed his rage, at the defeat and humiliation he had sustained since the preceding night.

"Mr. Horton," said Gerald Leslie, gravely, "Philip Treverton and I had a very serious purpose in coming to you here this evening. We come to make an appeal to your generosity, and your sense of manly honour. Will you listen patiently to that appeal?"

"You are free to speak," replied Augustus, haughtily, and throwing away his cigar, he folded his arms, and placed himself against a pillar that bordered the window, as if prepared to listen, but as if determined not to be convinced.

"I appeal to you then, in the presence of your sister and your cousin, and in that of Mrs. Montresor, whose sentiments, I know, are opposed to the cruel system of barter, which has in my case deprived a father of his beloved and only daughter – I appeal to every better feeling of your nature, and I ask if my child, Cora, is to suffer for one hour for the infamy of that man, Silas Craig? Restore her to freedom, before I institute proceedings to invalidate the illegal sale of my property, which was seized upon for a debt I never owed."

Augustus Horton laughed bitterly.

"All this is very fine," he said; "but as Miss Cora Leslie has chosen to run away from her rightful owner, it is not in my power to give her up – even if I wished it!"

Would you restore her to me if she were found?" asked Gerald Leslie.

"No."

"You would not? Remember, we are rich, and I would give you back your fifty thousand dollars, or double that sum, if you pleased."

"Curse your paltry dollars!" cried Augustus. "It was revenge I wanted to buy with my money; revenge for the insult your slave-daughter dared to inflict upon me. And am I to be balked of that revenge to the very last? No, I repeat, that were Cora recaptured to-night, I would not give her up."

"You would not?"

"I would not; and what is more I could not, for she is no longer mine."

"No longer yours!"

"No; I have given her away!"

"Given her away!"

"Yes, to my sister Adelaide, yonder, who has good reason to hate her, and who will make her feel what it is to be a slave. Trust a woman for that! With me she would have lived the life of a duchess; as my sister's property she will be a lady's-maid – a drudge. Heaven knows how low she may sink. It may please her mistress to send your brilliant and accomplished daughter to the kitchen to wait upon the cook."

Gerald Leslie writhed at this insulting speech.

"Miss Horton," he exclaimed, "surely, surely your woman's nature revolts at such words as these. Why do you not speak? You were once my daughter's friend; for pity's sake remember that!"

During the whole of this dialogue, Adelaide Horton had sat perfectly still, her head bent over her work, as if she heard nothing of what was going forward; but a close observer might have perceived that her bosom heaved with suppressed emotion, and that her small hand trembled as she endeavoured to continue her work.

This had not been lost upon Mortimer Percy, who had been for some time intently watching his cousin.

Suddenly she raised her head, in order to reply to Gerald Leslie.

"I can only answer you in the words of my brother, Mr. Leslie," she said; "I cannot restore Cora Leslie to you even if I would, for she is no longer mine. I, too, have given her away."

Augustus started at these words.

"You, Adelaide!" he exclaimed.

"Yes! You gave her to me for a lady's-maid. I had been long seeking for an opportunity of repairing the injury which I did her upon that fatal day when I allowed a school girl's folly to get the better of my reason. I have given her to her husband, Gilbert Margrave!"

She rose as she said this, and opened the door of an adjoining apartment, and beckoned to someone within.

Gilbert Margrave and Cora Leslie entered the room.

"My brother did not think of searching his own house for the runaway slave," said Adelaide, smiling. "The abduction of last night was planned by Mr. Margrave and myself, and it was agreed that he should bring her here as the last place in which her pursuers would be likely to seek her."

Mortimer Percy started from his chair, and, crossing the room, clasped his cousin in his arms.

"Did you indeed do this, Adelaide?" he exclaimed; "did you indeed? And will you forgive me for my conduct? Heaven knows what pain it has given me, for I have always loved you dearly."

"I deserved all I have suffered, Mortimer," replied Adelaide, disengaging herself gently from her cousin's enthusiastic embrace; "but I have done all in my power to repair the error of a moment. Cora is free; free to sail for England with her betrothed husband."

"Dear, generous girl," murmured the Octoroon, taking Adelaide's hand in hers; "far away, in that free and happy country, I shall remember your noble conduct."

"And you shall see us in England before long, my dear Miss Leslie," said Mortimer, "if my cousin will allow her most penitent swain to conduct her on a bridal tour through Europe. Mr. Leslie, you, I suppose, will accompany your daughter to England."

"I shall," replied Gerald; "thanks to the providential return of my dear friend and partner here, I shall be rich enough to establish myself on British ground, leaving to him the cares of the plantation."

"Which will be heavy enough to keep him out of gambling-houses," said Philip Treverton, with a smile.

Augustus Horton felt that his defeat and humiliation were complete. He had no alternative but to put the best possible face upon the matter, and he was wise enough to accept this alternative with a tolerable grace.

"Mr. Margrave," he said, "let all ill will be forgotten between us. Miss Leslie will tell you that all is fair in love as in war. We have played a desperate game, for the sake of yonder lady's smiles, and I have lost. So be it. I can but submit to my defeat, and congratulate you on your superior fortune. There is my hand."

Gilbert and Augustus shook hands. Both men felt the hollowness of the ceremonial.

Gerald Leslie's carriage, with Toby as the driver, was in waiting to convey the happy trio to Lake Pont Chartrain; and in three days they were to leave Louisiana in an English steamer. Philip Treverton asked permission to accompany his old partner to the pavilion. Mortimer Percy remained with his cousin Adelaide.

Two days after this happy evening, Mortimer led his fair bride to the altar.

The ceremonial took place thus hurriedly in order that Cora – the Octoroon, the once despised slave – might officiate as bridesmaid at her old schoolfellow's wedding.

The bride was given away by her brother Augustus, and Gilbert Margrave acted as "best man" to the bridegroom.

On the day following, Gilbert, Cora, and Gerald Leslie were to bid adieu to New Orleans. The marriage ceremony was performed with great splendour, and a sumptuous banquet was given by Augustus Horton to the most distinguished inhabitants of New Orleans.

It had been intended that Cora Leslie should appear at this banquet; and there was considerable curiosity felt upon the subject by the guests who knew the leading particulars of her story, and who were anxious to see the heroine of such romantic adventures.

They were disappointed, however, for, just as the bride was taking her place at the table, the Quadroon slave, Myra, slipped a note into her hand.

It was from Cora, and ran thus:–

"DEAREST ADELAIDE, – Forgive me if I have disobeyed you in withdrawing from your brilliant assembly. All your visitors are not as generous as yourself; and there may be many amongst your guests whose prejudices would be outraged by the presence of a daughter of the despised race. I have a sacred duty to perform before leaving Louisiana; and I go with Gilbert to fulfil it during the hours of your festivity.

"Ever and ever your affectionate

"CORA."

The reader may, perhaps, guess the duty which called Cora Leslie from that festive party.

Deep in the bosom of that wood at Iberville, in which Gilbert Margrave and Augustus Horton had met some months before, Cora knelt with her lover beside the wooden cross which alone marked the spot where the martyred Francilia lay.

Mournful were the tears which the freeborn Englishman and his betrothed bride wept upon the grave of the victim of slavery. But the star of hope shone above the tomb and a prophetic whisper in the hearts of both, told of a day when the terrible institution which enables man to traffic in the body and soul of his fellow men, should be only a dark memory of the past.

* * * * * * *

Early next day a happy group stood upon the deck of a large steamer, which was speeding away from New Orleans.

Already the queen city of the Mississippi was fading in the horizon, the white walls of villas, and the steeples of churches melting in the distance.

Cora Leslie stood with her arm linked in that of her father, and with her betrothed husband by her side.

A little way behind them, laden with shawls, parasols, and books, and proud to be of service to his young mistress, stood Toby, the mulatto; no longer a slave, but a happy attendant on those he loved.

A few weeks after this another vessel steamed out of the New Orleans harbour, bearing some who have been familiar to us; but this steamer was bound for the sunny shores of France.

Paul Crivelli and his cousin Camillia decided on leaving New Orleans until the Spanish girl had recovered from the shock of her father's death. They had consented therefore to accompany Armand Tremlay and Pauline, who, after considerable persuasion, had been induced to become the wife of her old lover without further delay.

Silas Craig left New Orleans in the dead of the night. None knew whither he went, and few cared to discover. He had so contrived as to convey away the whole of his wealth, and if the possession of gold, each coin of which is branded with meanness and dishonour, can bring happiness, the usurer may be a happy man.

But let him not hug himself in the security of his hiding place, the bloodhounds of the law are on his track. His departure revealed the secrets of his past life. The gambling-house in Columbia Street, and all the nefarious practices which had been permitted in that haunt of vice, were brought to the light of day. A warrant was issued for the lawyer's apprehension, and his pursuers do not yet despair of dragging him to justice.

Heaven help him, should he ever be so rash as to return to New Orleans! Once in the hands of his infuriated fellow citizens, Silas Craig would have to endure the horrors of Lynch law.

We have little more to say. Those of whom we have written, live to receive the reward of their own actions. Cora is a happy wife in our own dear native land – happy in the society of the father she loves, secure in the devotion of her proud English husband.

Camillia and Paul are the stars of a Parisian circle. Rich, accomplished, and handsome, the young Spaniard and his wife are admired and caressed by all who know them, but they have no friends whom they regard with the same affection as Armand and Pauline Tremlay.

Our story is finished. We have not been dealing with the shadowy woes of fiction, but with the real sorrows that have wrung and tortured human hearts, the hearts of our oppressed brothers and sisters.

If any line which we have written has gained one convert to the cause of freedom, we have not written in vain, and the feeling of regret with which we bid adieu to the kind and indulgent readers who have sympathised with the sufferings, of which we have told, will be mingled with the happy consciousness, that our labour has not been wasted, and that we have made friends for the great cause of Liberty *versus* Slavery, as well as for CORA, the OCTOROON.